Pelican Books
The Spell of Mathematics

W. J. Reichmann was born in Chelsea in 1920 and
now lives in Acton. He has been a practising
statistician in commerce and industry for some years,
and is a director of a number of companies with a
wide variety of interests. He is a Fellow of the Royal
Statistical Society, and a member of the Chartered
Institute of Secretaries, the Market Research Society,
the Mathematical Association, and other professional
societies. He has edited an accountancy journal and
contributed articles to other journals. His other books
are *The Fascination of Numbers* (published in 1957), *Use
and Abuse of Statistics* (1961, available in Pelicans), also
Calculus Explained (1964), and *The Spell of Mathematics*
(1967).

W. J. Reichmann

The Spell of Mathematics

Penguin Books

Penguin Books Ltd, Harmondsworth,
Middlesex, England
Penguin Books Australia Ltd, Ringwood,
Victoria, Australia

First published by Methuen 1967
Published in Pelican Books 1972

Copyright © W. J. Reichmann, 1967

Made and printed in Great Britain by
Richard Clay (The Chaucer Press) Ltd,
Bungay, Suffolk
Set in Monotype Times

To the Memory of my Mother

Contents

Prologue

Multiplication is Vexation
   Division is as bad,
The Rule of Three doth puzzle me
   And Practice makes me mad.

Anon. 1570

So was it then with me, and so will be
With Poets ever. Mighty is the charm
Of those abstractions to a mind beset
With images, and haunted by herself,
And specially delightful unto me
Was that clear synthesis built up aloft
So gracefully; even then when it appeared
Not more than a mere plaything, or a toy
To sense embodied: not the thing it is
In verity, an independent world,
Created out of pure intelligence.

The Prelude, Wordsworth

Ah! Why, ye Gods, should two and two make four?

Dunciad, Pope

Preface

Mathematics has an extraordinary fascination for its enthusiasts. This in itself has always been a source of wonderment to those others who, remembering their class-room agonies, would more readily subscribe to the cry of the anonymous Elizabethan quoted on the previous page. How, they wonder, could Wordsworth bring himself to describe geometrical abstractions as possessing charms of their own?

This is not a simple question to answer, for it is as difficult to understand other people's enthusiasms as it is easy to be philosophical about their troubles. The mathematician himself has difficulty in attempting to describe, let alone explain, the fullness of this fascination. Nor can it be analysed in any detail; it has an elusive quality which defies definition.

It is, however, possible to isolate and identify many diverse aspects of mathematics each of which has an intriguing appeal of its own. None of these can alone account for the depth of satisfaction which mathematics as a whole can provide, but taken together they do nevertheless present a panorama of the variety, diversity and aesthetic quality of mathematics. The overall fascination is more than the sum of the separate effects, but it arises imperceptibly out of them.

Many interesting features are included in these pages; some old favourites, some new ones and others running under different colours. They have been chosen for their power to excite the intellect or to point out the relationships, often unexpected, which exist between different branches of mathematics.

The selection and the emphasis accorded the subject matter introduced must, for the very reasons mentioned above, be based primarily on personal preference. This does at least have the merit of producing a natural selection rather than an artificial one consisting of features which *ought* to be interesting. Others would doubtless have made different choices, and there is much more which I would like to have been able to include. Nevertheless there is sufficient here to illustrate the absorbing felicities which abound in mathematics.

Travelling abroad helps to put our personal existences into proper perspective. We may be delighted, astonished or intrigued by the novelty of many of the things we see or hear. In much the same way a journey through the wider territories of mathematics may both astonish and delight us, thus clothing with unexpected colour the seeming drabness of the more restricted areas of repetitive and other mechanical vexations.

1. The Spell of Mathematics

Surprise and the unexpected rank high in the fabric of mathematical fascination, whether originating in the nature of mathematics itself or in the remarkable relationships between its different branches or, more simply, in paradoxes and puzzles. Here then is an appetizing example which hitherto appears to have escaped comment.

Most people would doubtless claim to understand the simple statement that the temperature in London on a particular day in summer was twice as great as it was on some other specified day in winter. If, for instance the temperature was 40°F. on Christmas Day and 80°F. on Midsummer Day, then it was twice as great at Midsummer as it was at Christmas. So far, so good – or is it?

It is worth pausing for a moment to study this comparison carefully and to see whether it contains anything to which it is possible to take exception. There are no tricks in the words. Then, by the simple operation of converting the temperature readings from the Fahrenheit to the Centigrade scale, we can reveal an oddity which few readers will have anticipated.

Christmas	40°F	4·4°C
Midsummer	80°F	26·7°C
Ratio	1 : 2	1 : 6+

A comparison of the Centigrade readings now shows that the temperature at Midsummer was over six times greater than at Christmas, whereas the Fahrenheit readings show that it was only twice as great! No wonder the meteorologists are adopting the Centigrade scale – it gives much more satisfactory weather reports!

This is an unexpected outcome of a veritable commonplace. Comparisons of temperature, even if not expressed in actual ratios, are made daily with monotonous inevitability. Yet such comparisons are seemingly based upon suspiciously insecure foundations. Which is right – Fahrenheit or Centigrade – or neither?

These questions involve a number of considerations, some of which are not strictly mathematical, and these will be dealt with more appropriately in the last chapter. Here it is merely desired to indicate the kind of surprise which will reward even such a minor venture into mathematics.

An important effect of the above unexpected result is that it will almost certainly stimulate us to make a closer inspection of the ideas and principles upon which the different temperature scales are based. This is true of mathematics generally. While a surprising result will provoke a sense of satisfaction in itself, it will also invite the intellect to search for similar examples. Eventually this invitation will become a veritable incitement. Paradoxes often arise out of what appear to be the simplest of considerations. Yet, as here, they usually serve to indicate a problem of unsuspected depth and to throw perplexing doubt upon hitherto unquestioned apparent facts.

Another surprise awaits us if we speculate about such a girdle as Puck, with forty minutes to spare, might have put about the earth in his search for Oberon's love-in-idleness. The equator is some 24,900 miles long. If this were a perfect circle (which it is not) and a girdle instead of an imaginary line, how much longer would the girdle have to be so that all its points were at a uniform distance of one foot from the earth? Surely a matter of some miles at least? Not at all – about 6¼ feet!

This seems a ridiculous assertion until we take a look at the mathematics involved. Then all is plain girdle-making. For if the radius of the equatorial circle is r feet, then its perimeter or length is $2\pi r$ feet. The radius of the increased girdle will be $(r + 1)$ feet and its length will be $2\pi(r + 1)$ feet. The difference between the original and the increased lengths will thus be 2π feet or just about 6¼ feet.

What is perhaps even more surprising is the fact that a girdle drawn at the arctic circle, although much shorter than that at the equator, would also have to be lengthened by exactly the same amount of about 6¼ feet if it were required to stand off from the earth at a uniform distance of one foot. One would not, without carrying out the calculations, expect that the lengthening of the girdle by so small an amount would permit it to stand clear of the earth by as much as a foot. In fact, however, the calculations show that the effect of lengthening the girdle in no way depends upon the original length of the girdle.

This is puzzling to the intuition, but the mystery is simply dispelled by the use of the formula for the circumference of a circle. It involves no very deep problem. It does, however, show how unreliable human intuition can be and indicates the manner in which mathematics can help to correct its misconceptions.

Surprise is only one of the spurs to the enjoyment of mathematics. There are many others. Some of them are very subtle indeed and perhaps only vaguely realized, but between them they nevertheless exercise a potent influence in the stimulation of acute mental concentration.

There is no lack of anecdotes about the apparently absurd behaviour of mathematical geniuses whose absorption in their researches could exclude practically all other thoughts from their minds.

Sir Isaac Newton is said once to have been seen with a bridle trailing from his hand, blissfully unaware that the horse, which he had been leading, had slipped from its harness. On another occasion it is said that he went to fetch some wine for the dinner table but that on the way to the cellar he became so deep in thought that he completely forgot his errand and his astonished guests were left to fend for themselves.

Plutarch relates that Archimedes, apart from a disregard for his meals (a symptom normally associated more readily with a disturbance of the affections by causes other than mathematical fervour), would also treat the rites attendant upon bathing with such unconcern as to draw geometrical designs in the anointing oils. Tradition also asserts that even in the sacking of Syracuse when he was at the very point of death, he calmly continued his deliberations upon some absorbing problem completely impervious to the menace of the Roman soldiery.

Lest it be thought that it is necessary to reach back into the hoary mists of history to uncover suitable examples, we may cite the behaviour in more recent times of John von Neumann. It is said to have been not uncommon for him to become so engrossed in his problems, whilst on a journey, that he often had to telephone home to check where he was supposed to be going.

All these men of course were giants of mathematical thought grappling with abstruse problems or theories of extreme complexity. Their apparently negative symptom of forgetfulness was in reality a sign of intense positive mental activity upon matters which they regarded as so much more sublime than those about which they were so unmindful.

Whether these stories are exaggerations or even whether they have any basis in fact is quite immaterial. The mere fact that such stories can circulate at all itself bears witness to the reality of the absorption which they serve to express and which has entered in varying degrees into the experience of those in whose circles the stories circulate.

For it is not only those whose lives are centred about mathematics who can experience the peculiar spellbinding fascination which the subject induces in its enthusiasts. It is surprising for example to learn that Napoleon, whenever the more celebrated and delectable intimate diversions permitted, would often find time between battles to indulge an odd delight in the contemplation of a book of logarithms. Perhaps he found these companions more consistently reliable than some others we might mention!

Doctor Johnson has admitted to finding great diversion in the practice of 'chymistry', but Boswell relates that Johnson also found much solace in the study of arithmetic. This combination of interests provides a useful analogy for there is every bit as much enjoyment and satisfaction to be derived from solving a mathematical problem for oneself as there is in personally carrying out a chemical experiment successfully.

An interest in mathematics is probably much more widely experienced than is generally realized. Distinction is often made between professional and amateur mathematicians, but this has no real meaning in relation to the enjoyment of mathematics and it is often as difficult to distinguish between them as it is between similar nominal categories in sport. In mathematics at least the distinction is certainly unreal.

A great many mathematical triumphs have been achieved in fields well beyond the call of duty for which so-called professionals receive payment. The true mathematician mathematizes because he wants to do so and not because he is paid to do so. Pierre de Fermat was almost certainly the greatest amateur mathematician of all time; yet his work was omitted from a book devoted to the mathematics of amateurs because 'he is too great to be described as an amateur'.

Mathematics indeed offers many attractions to almost any person who is not absolutely befuddled by numbers. But although we may sense its fascination in the strongest possible way, its spell is so elusive that we cannot adequately describe it or even account for its effect. How indeed can we explain or describe any of our enthusiasms and emotions – the transient taste of favourite delicacies, the subtle bouquet of fine wine, the ecstatic or deeply moving effect of music, the rare appreciation of art and beauty and the countless other exquisite pleasures and sensations which we are fortunate to experience. Among these lies the fascination of mathematics. None of them can be analysed but they are no less real for all that.

The fullest enjoyment of experience is an amalgam of emotions and sensations – one alone neither identifies nor satisfies. Sight, sound, smell and indefinable mental responses all combine to fix the peculiar essence of an occasion, so that the merest reminder of any one of these attributes will at once recall memories of the others. So does the appeal of mathematics have many facets each of which is capable of evoking the others often in circumstances when such an effect might be least expected.

Not every phrase of music will induce the same responsive thrill; nor perhaps can the repetition of any music ever again recapture quite the same response evoked by the very first hearing. Neither can the senses be ravished for long continuous periods. Emotions cannot run forever at peak level, for then all the peaks would merely form a new plateau. Pleasure is ephemeral and some forms are more fleeting than others. Yet mathematics is a constant delight. The freshness of its wonder may be recaptured and its magical quality and beauty of pattern may be rediscovered anew as often as we please. Indeed it always seems to come still brighter each time our acquaintance with it is renewed, just as the perfection of a fine silver candlestick stands revealed, after each new polish, apparently as fresh as on the day it was made.

Modern developments in mathematics, as in other sciences, have been so rapid and of such a diverse character that it is no longer possible, even if it ever were, to divide the sciences into separate and distinct compartments. Chemistry and biology overlap in the newer fields of research in biochemistry and many other sciences have found common ground from which have sprung up virtually new sciences. The physical structure of chemical elements is in some way connected with their chemical properties; we cannot disregard either aspect in our search for knowledge.

In the same way it is impossible to identify a clear-cut separation between pure and applied mathematics, although many principles do clearly have practical applications whereas others do not. By far the most refined pleasure is to be derived from the latter.

The difference between pure and applied mathematics, so far as it is distinguishable at all, has a parallel in the difference between abstract and descriptive music and in the difference between abstract and representational art forms. Some of the most sublime phrases of music have no literal translation or apparent point of contact with reality at all. This is music for the sake of music. We may sometimes have a shrewd suspicion that artists and composers of abstract forms work with their tongues in their cheeks and their fingers crossed – a difficult feat at the best of times. Certainly if such artists have the misfortune to see their subjects in the form in which they reproduce them it must be better for them to get it out of their systems. Yet the person who ridicules abstract art may well appreciate abstract music with no more positive rational justification.

There is no way of explaining this. Certainly we can enjoy mathematics for its own sake, and this enjoyment is perhaps heightened by an added quality which other forms of abstraction do not possess. Accomplished mathematicians take rare delight in developing highly sophisticated systems which do not have and are not intended to have any specific practical application. Yet many systems which were developed in this way subsequently proved to have practical uses as well.

If pure mathematics needed any other justification then this dividend of practical utility would suffice, but the truth is that pure mathematics can manage very well on its own. The Greek mathematicians were primarily philosophers and they were interested in mathematics solely in its relation to their philosophies. They had a hearty contempt for work and business affairs, an attribute not entirely lacking in today's society, and indeed in Boeotia those who committed the folly of dealing in commerce were banned from state service. Only the slaves worked.

The trends of mathematical thought current during particular periods appear to have reflected the general cultural standards of the respective periods. The quality of the Greek culture was far superior to that of the practical-minded Romans who followed, and it is perhaps significant that the Greeks did not regard what we now call applied mathematics as mathematics at all. Whitehead sarcastically commented that no Roman had ever lost his life, as had Archimedes, because of his absorption in a mathematical diagram, though it is possibly unfair to the Romans' good sense to blame them for that. Just so does the voluble but prejudiced guide at Delphi still expectorate as he dismisses a particular piece of statuary as mere Roman rubbish!

The appeal of mathematics results from or itself exercises some kind of selective process, although the selection may not be, and indeed probably is not, a conscious one. Some people have an inbred flair for numbers while others, who do not share that felicity, may nevertheless assimilate counting habits to such a degree that counting becomes automatic. They count the steps every time they climb the stairs, the number of turns when winding their watches and even more noticeably perhaps among children, the number of strawberries on each other's plates.

Learning to count comes as naturally, though not always with the same permanent success, as learning to talk, provided there is adequate instruction. This argues a receptiveness in the human mind for the rudiments of mathematics. The higher flights of more advanced mathematics are as distinct from such rudiments as sophisticated literature is distinct from learning to talk. But just as we can from simple beginnings develop our personal taste for literature, so we can also from the same lowly level gradually enlarge our private taste for mathematics.

It is as easy to lose oneself in mathematical study as in an enthralling book. A well-written novel will induce a familiarity with its characters far beyond the few details actually described. The reader shares the action with the characters. Familiarity with numbers helps us to trace the course of mathematical discoveries and to share in the delight of the pioneer mathematician just as if we had actually been present at the time of his discovery.

Words have an aesthetic quality dependent upon their shape, their sound or lyrical nature and their juxtaposition each to each. An author's style largely depends upon the way in which these qualities are exploited. Numbers are some of the words of mathematics with which we express our problems and theorems, but it soon becomes apparent to the alert student that numbers too have their own peculiar qualities.

It is indeed probably true that most readers are first attracted to mathematics through an interest in the behaviour of numbers or number theory. This is because this subject has an immediate impact. It is easy to visualize, if not at once to understand, the simpler relationships between certain kinds of numbers. That there should be such apparently regular patterns where there seems to be no reason for the regularity is itself a cause for wonder. Beyond this the regularity itself displays a beauty of symmetry which appeals direct to the intellect.

The interest thus aroused leads to ensnarement. Once we are interested in mathematics we cannot shed our involvement as if it were a garment. When we have admired the beauty awhile we are soon moved to seek out the underlying principles. From mere wonder the path is but a short one to the acceptance of the implied challenge to the intellect. This challenge and the satisfaction of meeting it provide two further aspects of the real appeal of mathematics. Yet a third aspect which is in a sense contained in the other two, is the delight of discovery.

The legendary antics of Archimedes in his unclothed state as the prototype absent-minded professor have come to symbolize the irrepressible joy of discovery. This joy is in no way restrained and may indeed be intensified when, as with Ho-ti's delight at his son's discovery of roast pig, the discoveries are fortuitous.

Most of the routes through mathematics have already been marked out and it might appear that we have only to recognize the markings. Yet mathematics offers much more than a mere paper-chase. Mathematics cannot be enjoyed without some personal effort. One always has to do important things for oneself; always suspect the eager gentleman who offers to make your fortune for you.

A little effort will pay great dividends. We can make our own discoveries as we go along. What does it matter if someone else has been there before us? What does it matter to the athlete that he was not the first to run a four-minute mile? The effort he makes is no less real and his satisfaction is no less important. Every race calls for a new effort and every success is a new victory.

Although some discoveries may be loosely described as accidental it is an illusion to believe that this is true in general. Most advances in mathematics have resulted from the strenuous and brain-exhausting efforts of genius. James Sylvester describes how at one sitting he discovered a theory 'with a decanter of port wine to sustain nature's flagging energies, at the usual cost of racking thought – a brain on fire, and feet feeling, or feeling-less, as if plunged in an icy pail'.

It is given to but few men to know the triumphant ecstasy of original mathematical discovery. The distant peaks are hidden from all but these fortunate few. Those who conquer mighty mountains are the giants of mountaineering, but there are count-less others throughout the world indulging their love of rock climbing. They climb rocks because they enjoy doing it, and the Everest man is still a rock climber at heart.

There is plenty of mathematical climbing to do and the magical view of the peaks, once discerned, provides a powerful temptation to keep on climbing. There is an infinity in the variety of views which open up at different levels, and many side routes, invisible from lower levels, offer tantalizing invitations to exploration away from the main routes.

It is often surprising to discover the number and the diversity of methods by which a particular theorem may be proved or by which a problem can be solved. On the other hand a single principle or theorem may be found to have many different uses and applications and there are remarkable relationships between quite different processes.

This variety in the differing nature of respective processes and their often unexpected points of contact gives rise to a genuine aesthetic satisfaction. There is a beauty and elegance in mathematics which far transcends its technicalities. It is difficult to describe this elegance since, to paraphrase a noted cliché, the beauty of mathematics is in the mind of the beholder.

Bertrand Russell describes this as 'supreme beauty . . . cold and austere like that of sculpture . . . sublimely pure and capable of a stern perfection such as only the greatest art can show'. This describes but one facet of beauty; it fails to account for the warmer emotional response which mathematical contemplation can induce. Polya is quoted as saying that he regarded the elegance of a theorem as being directly proportional to the number of ideas which may be seen in it and inversely proportional to the effort it takes to see them. As elsewhere, elegance is the essence of sophisticated simplicity.

The great power of mathematics rests in its ability to confine many apparently complex problems within relatively simple capsule solutions. Even where it cannot provide such a satisfactory conclusion nevertheless its method, conciseness and discipline at least help to clarify the issues involved in the problem and perhaps to suggest approximate solutions within acceptable limits of error.

Mathematics is a powerful aid to the imagination in that it makes possible the measurement of dimensions (such as those of the earth) which we cannot see, and distances (such as light years) which the human mind cannot properly visualize. The problems of the universe can thus by mathematical facility be brought within the more familiar atmosphere of our own rooms.

Mathematics indeed offers a new language in which to describe scientific problems and theorems, a set of tools with which to tackle those problems and a guiding light to illuminate research into scientific theories generally. Knowledge serves the dual purpose of satisfying our curiosity while at the same time providing outlets for our creative forces in the use of the principles discovered. This is true in both pure and applied mathematics.

Even those problems which defiantly resist our every assault have a tantalizing mental ensnarement. These are the problems which we cannot leave alone and it is these indeed which induce a high degree of absorption. This absorption in extreme cases borders upon obsession, and it must at once be admitted that obsession is not to be admired. It may well destroy enjoyment by converting a lively interest into enslaved drudgery. Mathematics can be indulged to excess. Some people can see nothing but angles of elevation in the gracious temples of Greece. Stephen Leacock satirized this attitude in his story of the bitter disillusionment of the intellectual who realized only after his marriage that his wife could not solve quadratic equations! In real life, of course, such a sad defect is more damaging to the parental prestige of those expected to help out with the homework.

The pursuit of knowledge, however, has always exercised a strange yearning excitement upon the human mind and, if it is not carried to excess, it can prove to be the most sublime source of inner contentment. Mathematics helps to give this yearning a sense of direction, but it also tempers it with discipline.

Sir Francis Bacon said that mathematics makes a man 'subtile' and, although it may not be precisely clear what he meant by this, it is nevertheless certain that, except in the most intractable cases, mathematics sharpens the wits and generally tones up the processes of thought. It helps to develop a proper sense of proportion and provides a sound training in logic. It breeds an awareness that apparent facts should not be accepted at face value and a faculty of detachment with which such 'facts' may be appraised.

It is true that not everyone has subscribed to this view. The most outspoken in condemnation must surely have been the philosopher Sir William Hamilton, who should not be confused with his contemporary Sir William Rowan Hamilton, the mathematician famous for his work on quaternions. According to the former: 'Mathematics cannot conduce to logical habits' and 'an excessive study of mathematics absolutely incapacitates the mind for those intellectual energies which philosophy and life require'.

While everyone is entitled to his own opinion, the above statement does appear to be the nonsense of prejudice. Measured against modern standards the older ideas of philosophy often appear appallingly naïve, being based more upon mystical conjecture than upon scientific principles of reality. Mathematics, although not the final arbiter, was to show that many of these previously accepted ideas were untenable. If anyone desired to cling to the outdated concepts, he could do so only by denying the evidence of mathematics. No doubt our present-day ideas, both in mathematics and in philosophy, will appear naïve to commentators a few centuries hence. In the meantime we prefer to accept Voltaire's opinion that imagination is the very stuff of mathematics and that 'there was far more imagination in the head of Archimedes than there was in that of Homer'.

If any evidence of the imaginative essence of mathematics were required, this must surely already have been provided by the rapid and remarkable developments within mathematics during the last few decades. The variety and sophistication of these is astonishing. Whole new vistas have opened up and this in turn has awakened a more active awareness of mathematics generally.

The very structure of mathematics is now regarded as being quite different from what it was once thought to be. At one time, for example, geometry was distinguished simply and clearly from algebra. There was, so to speak, only one of each and they were thought to comprise distinct and separate categories. Euclid's was the only geometry, and the familiar algebra by which the ubiquitous and inconsequential characters *a* and *b* were enabled to dig fields or to fill baths, was the only algebra.

Today it is recognized that there is a close affinity between the two subjects and that there are different geometries and different algebras. The original forms of geometry and algebra have lost their reputation of uniqueness in the recognition that they are but special cases of more general forms. Modern developments in set theory have been heralded as providing a basis for the co-ordination of mathematics as a whole. While this claim has not as yet been fully substantiated it is certainly true that many propositions can be most easily translated into set language and that it does provide a considerable degree of co-ordination.

Prometheus, who is more renowned for his exploit in stealing the Olympian fire, is also credited in legend with the equally inspiring deed of passing on mathematics to mankind. But mathematics is a lively and growing art. It appears to stem more from man's imagination than from any higher source. It is perhaps because of this that the appeal of mathematics is essentially personal. Bernard Shaw once wrote that it was the making of music personal to a man which made that man a musician. The same personal involvement exists between mathematics and mathematicians.

Although a great deal of mathematics is complex and difficult, particularly in its more esoteric aspects, nevertheless there is much which appears difficult yet is disarmingly simple once it is understood. The realization that one is able to cope with problems, which but a little previously had seemed impossible even to approach, is most revealing of one's own self. This is the joy of self-discovery, not self-indulgence.

Just so must Oedipus have felt when he had guessed the answer to the riddle of the Theban Sphinx and she, duly mortified, had dashed herself to fragments in the valley below. We do not know what we can do until we try, although we must not expect examiners to follow the petulant example of the Sphinx, nor should we dwell too much upon the moral that, since so much was to depend upon it, Oedipus would have done better to have got the answer wrong.

2. Proof and Spoof

The ancient Greeks regarded mathematics with religious reverence. In particular they thought of numbers much in the same way as they thought of the Olympian gods, as having distinctive personalities of their own. It is easy enough, from our modern vantage-point, to ridicule their beliefs. Yet when one takes a closer look at the evidence in the peculiarities of number relationships and the apparent harmony between mathematics and many physical phenomena, it is easier to understand why they were misled into their belief, just as an awe-inspiring visit to Delphi in a thunderstorm makes it easier to understand why they believed in the powers of the gods themselves.

The gods were accorded a reality and a personification in the attributes of nature. Numbers and geometrical principles were thought to have a similar although not identical relevance. This belief seriously hampered the development of mathematics and it is only in relatively recent times that mathematics has finally divorced itself from its external obligations to gain a freedom of astonishing variety.

The Greeks made a vital contribution to mathematics, however, in their insistence upon the rigorous logical proof of their theorems. While this too may have had a damping-down effect upon mathematical development, it nevertheless had the salutary effect of instilling into mathematical thought the recognition of the absolute necessity of logical consistency. This consistency and the discipline it imposes are as proper in mathematics as a regard for truth in its wider sense is proper in our moral relationships.

This regard for logic was derived from, and itself accentuated, the Greek belief that mathematical principles were ideas and that these were of far greater importance and significance than any application to which they might be directed.

Superficially, geometry appears as a practical science since it often involves the construction of figures and has such useful practical applications. None the less geometry is essentially a science of ideas; the constructions are made simply to assist our thought. Lines representing dimensions in geometry are used in much the same way as are letters in algebra as part of a language for discussing or depicting mathematical principles.

The Greeks placed mathematical thought above mere physical applications. Archimedes was responsible for many engineering wonders produced for the defence of his native Syracuse. These were the results of his mathematical deliberations and Plutarch tells us that he 'possessed so high a spirit, so profound a soul . . . [that] repudiating as sordid and ignoble the whole trade of engineering, he placed his whole affection and ambition in those purer speculations . . . in which the only doubt can be whether the beauty and grandeur of the subjects examined or the precision and cogency of the methods and means of proof most merit our admiration'.

In all science there are two main methods of investigation. These are induction, allied with analogy, and deduction, based upon strict logic. There is a world of difference between them. Induction is the process of inferring general laws from observations of particular instances, and analogy is reasoning from apparently similar cases. Neither process provides proof. Deduction is the process of logical reasoning from an accepted premise or from one 'proved' fact to another.

Most sciences have to depend largely upon induction. An experiment will show, for example, that water boils at a temperature of $100°C$. Subject to certain conditions all subsequent experiments will show that water always boils at this temperature. Accordingly we accept that this happens and say that the boiling-point of water is $100°$. We cannot, however, establish a logical proof that this is correct. Always is for ever. We cannot be absolutely certain; we never really go beyond the stage of experimentation and we often have to revise our scientific theories to accord with subsequent discoveries.

The very essence of mathematics is that its laws and principles are logically consistent. This forms an acceptable basis on which to proceed, although in a later chapter it will be necessary to examine it more closely. This is a surprise in store for later consumption.

We are on surer ground, however, in rejecting induction as a part of formal mathematical proof. It is easy to see why this should be so from two interesting examples drawn from the theory of numbers.

Leonhard Euler hoped to find some formula which would always generate prime numbers. He experimented with the expression

$$n^2 - n + 41$$

For all positive integral values of n from 1 to 39 inclusive this expression does generate prime numbers exclusively. Yet even this is not sufficient to justify the assumption that all integral values of n will do so. In fact it can be seen by inspection that the expression will generate a composite number when n is 41. For values above $n = 41$, there is no apparent pattern in the occurrences of prime numbers. It can indeed be proved that no integral algebraic expression can represent prime numbers exclusively.

The second example concerns Fermat's discovery that numbers of the form $2^x + 1$ (where $x = 2^n$) are prime for values of $n = 0, 1, 2, 3$ and 4 respectively. He could not find any factor of the number generated by the value $n = 5$. Encouraged by this and the insidious suggestions of induction, he expressed the opinion that all numbers of this form are probably also prime. Unfortunately Fermat stopped too soon. His proposition is, in fact, false for the value $n = 5$.

Lest it be thought that Fermat could easily have verified this for himself, it may be noted that although the first three numbers derived from this expression are 3, 5, and 17 (when $n = 0, 1$ and 2 respectively), the next two numbers 257 and 65,537 show a rapid rate of increase. When $n = 5$, the relative Fermat number is 4,294,967,297.

Anyone might be excused for failing to find the factors of this number. Euler, having proved that the factor, if any, must itself be of a particular form, was able subsequently to reduce the work involved considerably. He discovered that this number has the factor 641. In defence of Fermat (though it is doubtful whether such a mind requires defending) it must be noted that he did not claim that the number actually was prime; he said merely that it seemed to be. This is the limit to the significance of the contribution which induction can make towards finding proofs.

Induction is rejected by mathematics only as a purported method of proof. Any so-called proof which relied entirely upon induction would be spoof, not proof.

All that which passed muster as mathematics before the Greeks took it in hand was apparently inductive and they would have nothing to do with it in that form. Yet many of the earlier achievements are really breath-taking. The construction of such remarkable architectural marvels as the Pyramids of Egypt and the beehive tombs of Mycenae was based upon principles derived by induction. The builders were satisfied that the principles were viable and, although they might not have been able to prove that the latter were logically satisfactory, the builders must have had a competent notion of what they were doing. No doubt they learned from their mistakes!

In its own right, as an experimental process or as a source of inspiration to the imagination, induction has immense value in helping to develop mathematical ideas. Many great theorems, which were eventually proved rigorously by logical deduction, found their origins in a process of induction or analogy.

There has always been some dispute as to the exact value of induction and the propriety of admitting it to the inner councils of mathematical research. Yet its effect seems to spice the resultant mixture rather than to dilute it. Even if extremists wished to ban it from mathematical thought entirely, they would be unable to do so. Our thoughts cannot be tamed in this way; indeed mathematics in particular and life in general would be very dull if they could.

Observation of specific examples of the peculiarity of number relationships may be expected to act as a spur to research in order to discover whether they are exceptional cases or whether they are particular cases of general relationships. It is a natural step to look first for other similar results. If we find these, as Euler and Fermat did, then we shall have within our grasp the beginnings of a theory warranting further research to see whether it can be proved as a formal theorem. But this is as much as induction can do – it can test the pupils for suitability to sit an examination but it cannot give out the passes.

Deduction is the only means of proof acceptable in mathematics, although it may make its contribution through a number of different methods. All methods, however, have certain characteristics in common. The process starts with a premise which may be either an already proven proposition or an hypothesis or assumption which is taken as being self-evident. The proof then proceeds by strict logical reasoning until some other consistent proposition is established. The stages of a general proof are thus closely linked to each other with one proof leading on to another, the whole process providing a network of proof which is at once the framework and the cement of mathematical structure.

The deductive method is the only infallible one for establishing consistent propositions, but it is not of itself sufficient to guarantee that results achieved by its use are necessarily correct. This will depend as much upon the correctness of the premise. Mathematical philosophy entertains some doubts as to the bona fides of self-evidence but we shall defer discussion of this until a later chapter.

If a premise is incorrect the use of deductive methods will not and cannot cure its defect, although the formal appearance of its presentation may well give it a dangerous apparent validity.

It is also necessary to ensure that our logic is not at fault. There was once a man (so it is said) who always became inebriated when he drank whisky and water; so he changed his nightcap to gin and water, but he still got drunk. After he had again changed his reviver to rum and water only to find his legs as unsteady as ever, he concluded that it must be the water which was having such a dire effect upon him since this was the only factor common to all his drinks.

Subject, however, to our premise and the subsequent logic being correct, then we can assure ourselves that mathematics, alone of all the sciences, has a specific reliability in its conclusions. If we accept the premises as correct we may also accept the conclusions. As Lewis Carroll observed, those who do not accept such conclusions, having previously accepted the premises, should advisedly abandon Euclid and take to football instead.

It is appropriate to take our first example of straightforward deduction from Euclid's Elements. The fifth proposition of Book I, which was to become known as the *pons asinorum* (a slighting commentary upon the alleged inability of medieval students to progress beyond it), asserts: 'The angles at the base of an isosceles triangle are equal to one another; and if the equal sides be produced, the angles on the other side of the base shall be equal to one another.'

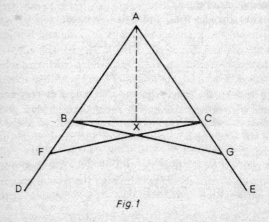

Fig. 1

In Fig. 1, the sides AB and AC in the triangle ACB are equal to one another. It is required to prove (i) the angles ABC and ACB are equal to one another, and (ii) the angles FBC and GCB are equal to one another, the sides AB and AC being produced to D and E respectively.

F is any point on the line BD. G is a point on the line CE such that AG = AF. The lines FC and GB are drawn as shown and this completes the necessary constructions.

Then in the triangles ACF and ABG we have:

$$AC = AB \text{ (by hypothesis)}$$
$$AF = AG \text{ (by construction)}$$
Angle FAG is common to both

Then, by Euclid's fourth proposition on the properties of equal triangles,

the base CF = the base BG
angle ACF = angle ABG
and   angle AFC = angle AGB

Since AF = AG (by construction) and AB = AC (by hypothesis) the remainders BF and CG must also be equal to one another (from Euclid's axiom 3 – if equals be taken from equals, the remainders are equal).

Then in the triangles BCF and CBG we have:

$$BF = CG \text{ (just proved)}$$
$$CF = BG \text{ (also proved above)}$$
angle BFC = angle CGB

Since these are the same angles as AFC and AGB respectively and these were proved above to be equal, accordingly:

The triangles BCF and CBG are equal triangles
and (again by Euclid's fourth proposition)
angle FBC = angle GCB (thus proving the second
proposition)
and   angle BCF = angle CBG

Since the whole angles ACF and ABG are equal; and the part angles BCF and CBG are equal then (by Euclid's axiom 3) the remainder angles must also be equal. That is

angle ACB = angle ABC (thus proving the first proposition).

Nowadays a different demonstration is employed, but the above demonstration is closer to the beginnings of geometry and is typical of the ingenious and logical manner in which Euclid systematically built up the whole structure of his Elements. He accepted an hypothesis here, permitted himself an axiom there, made such simple but effective constructions as were necessary and then used propositions which he had already proved as stepping-stones to more advanced proof.

The modern demonstration of the above theorem proceeds by drawing AX so that it bisects the angle BAC. Then in the triangles ABX and ACX we have:

$$AB = AC$$
AX is common to both
angle BAX = angle CAX by construction.

So, by Euclid's fourth proposition, the triangles are equal in all respects, whence the angle ABX is equal to the angle ACX. The equality of the external angles then follows as a corollary depending upon Euclid's thirteenth proposition that adjacent angles on one side of a straight line are together equal to two right angles, the adjacent angles being called the supplements of each other. The angles DBC and ECB are thus equal to each other since they are supplements respectively of the equal angles ABX and ACX.

This demonstration is easier to follow as it does not require the instrusion of the points F and G. The method is accordingly less involved and provides an alternative structure alongside the *pons asinorum*, although the crossing of the latter, like the crossing of the Rubicon, which is itself now crossed regularly by speeding motor-cars, has long since lost any real significance it may once have had as a bar to progress. It also serves to illustrate that a theorem may often be demonstrated in more than one way. This multiplicity of opportunity, although aided by ingenuity, arises primarily out of the many inter-relationships between the separate properties of isosceles triangles.

Another example of a straightforward deductive process provides an indication of how a result, eventually established deductively, may be suggested by induction.

An arithmetic progression is a sequence of quantities which increase or decrease by a common difference. Thus, in the sequence of odd numbers

1 3 5 7 9 · · · ·

the common difference between consecutive terms is 2. It may be observed that if the first term of a sequence is a (in this instance $a = 1$) and the common difference is d (here $d = 2$)

$$\text{1st term} = a + 0d = 1 + 0 = 1$$
$$\text{2nd term} = a + 1d = 1 + 2 = 3$$
$$\text{3rd term} = a + 2d = 1 + 4 = 5$$

and so on.

This suggests a general pattern. That is, the coefficient of d in any term is always less by one than the number of the term in the sequence; and that, generally, the nth term is $a + (n-1)d$.

We can now proceed to establish a formula for the sum of any given number of consecutive terms in any arithmetic progression of which a is the first term, l is the last term, and there are n terms. This sum may be expressed as

$$s = a + (a + d) + (a + 2d) + \ldots + (l - 2d) + (l - d) + l$$

This in itself is not in a general form and would require a great deal of work for each specific calculation. Yet it is simplicity itself to derive a general form from this expression by an ingenious twist. For, merely by reversing the order of the terms in the above series, we have

$$s = l + (l - d) + (l - 2d) + \ldots + (a + 2d) + (a + d) + a$$

Then by adding the two series, term by term, we obtain the convenient series in which all the terms are the same. That is

$$2s = (a + l) + (a + l) + (a + l) + \ldots$$
$$+ (a + l) + (a + l) + (a + l)$$

Then since there are n terms

$$2s = n(a + l)$$
$$\text{and } s = \frac{n}{2}(a + l)$$

Furthermore, since $l = a + (n-1)d$ (being the nth term)

$$s = \frac{n}{2}[2a + (n-1)d]$$

This is a general formula which will provide the sum of a series merely by the substitution of the relevant values of a, d, and n. It is not necessary to list all the terms of the series; nor is it necessary to know the value of the last term.

This again demonstrates that deduction and ingenuity go hand in hand. The idea of reversing the series is so elegantly simple that anyone can follow its application without difficulty, but it must undoubtedly have called for a ready and lively imagination when it was first conceived.

An indirect value of induction sometimes manifests itself in that, when the deduction based upon the induction is complete, the actual proof may itself reveal some other relationship which was not even suspected at the induction stage. Thus we may suspect, because it holds for so many values of n, that

$$1^3 + 2^3 + 3^3 + \ldots + n^3 = (1 + 2 + 3 + \ldots n)^2$$

For example

$$1^3 + 2^3 + 3^3 + 4^3 = 100 = (1 + 2 + 3 + 4)^2$$

It can in fact be proved that, for any value of n, the sum of the series of the cubes of the natural numbers to n terms is

$$\left(\frac{n(n+1)}{2}\right)^2$$

Thus when $n = 4$, the sum of the series of cubes is

$$\left(\frac{4 \times 5}{2}\right)^2 = 100$$

This result is based upon the formula for the sum of an arithmetic progression as shown above, for when $n = 4$, $a = 1$ and $d = 1$, the expression

$$\frac{n}{2}(2a + (n-1)d) \text{ simplifies to } \frac{4 \times 5}{2}$$

The result shows that the sum of the series for a given number of terms may be easily computed by taking the square of half the product of that number and its next greatest number. This fact would not have been obvious from mere induction.

It is not always possible to adopt a direct method of deductive proof. It is, however, sometimes possible to attack a problem from the rear by a system of indirect proof or *reductio ad absurdum*. A very fine distinction is sometimes drawn between indirect proof and *reductio ad absurdum* in that the latter shows the falsity of an assumption by obtaining from it a clear-cut absurdity, whereas indirect proof establishes the proof of an assumption by showing that the opposite assumption is false. In fact, this comes to very much the same thing.

The method is ingeniously based upon the provisional acceptance of some assumption which it then proceeds to demolish by showing that it leads to a contradiction. This is not unlike the cunning of a barrister who apparently accepts a statement by the accused and then calmly leads him to his destruction on the strength of it. As soon as the accused makes a further statement which is inconsistent with the first, Counsel pounces with: 'Ah, but you said . . .' and the abashed prisoner is hauled off to the cells for his trouble.

One of the most elegant proofs of this type is the proof, due to Euclid, that the number of primes is infinite. It is a remarkably simple proof, but its implications are tremendous.

The proof assumes that the assertion is wrong. Let it be assumed that the number of primes is *not* infinite and let p be the greatest prime number. Then the product (which we shall call N) of all the prime numbers:

$$N = 1.2.3.5.7\ldots p$$

is divisible by each of these primes. Consequently the number $(N + 1)$ cannot be divisible by *any* of these primes.

Hence $(N + 1)$ is either itself a prime or is divisible by some prime greater than p. These are the only two possibilities and, in either case, p is not the greatest possible prime number. This contradicts the original assumption; hence the original assumption must be wrong because it leads to such a contradiction. So the number of primes *is* infinite.

This proof, which is concerned with a whole infinity of numbers, is achieved with great economy. Another elegant proof of this type is the demonstration that a quadratic equation cannot have more than two roots; this is included in Chapter 7.

The indirect method can also be used to show that Euler's attempt to find a rational algebraic expression, which would generate primes exclusively, was doomed to disappointment. This demonstration differs, however, in that it is sufficient to show that any such proposed expression will produce at least one non-prime.

Let it be assumed that such an expression exists, being in the general form:

$$a + bx + cx^2 + dx^3 + \ldots$$

(it being understood that some of the coefficients may be zero). Let the value of this expression be s when $x = m$. Thus:

$$s = a + bm + cm^2 + dm^3 + \ldots$$

Again, when $x = m + ns$, the value of the expression will be:

$$t = a + b(m + ns) + c(m + ns)^2 + d(m + ns)^3 + \ldots$$

which may be transformed by multiplying out and changing the order of terms to:

$$t = (a + bm + cm^2 + dm^3 + \ldots) + A$$

where A represents all the other terms all of which are multiples of s. But the expression within the brackets is equal to s by our original hypothesis. Consequently the whole expression is a multiple of s and the number produced is not a prime.

This result is achieved no matter what expression we select for testing. Every expression will thus produce at least one non-prime. No expression, therefore, can generate primes exclusively.

One particular form of the indirect method, much beloved of Fermat in his researches into number theory, is what he called the method of infinite descent. This, as might be expected, displays an ingenuity of high distinction. Our previous examples have illustrated the demolition of false assumptions by showing that they depended upon inherent logical inconsistencies. The method of infinite descent, however, forces an argument to a numerical limit and then shows that, if the assumption were correct, the process would go beyond the limit, which, of course, is impossible.

In a typical example the proof of the impossibility of an assumption proceeds by making its possibility depend firstly upon the existence of some positive integral value of a variable quantity. It then shows that there must also necessarily be a lower positive integral value and that this process can be carried on *indefinitely*. But the number of positive integers less than any given positive integer is *finite*. There is no positive integer lower than 1. Accordingly the process can *not* be carried on indefinitely. The contradiction is thus exposed.

In effect the nub of the matter is the requirement that there is necessarily a positive integral value which is lower than any other integer. This is patently absurd since there is no integer lower than 1.

The progress towards the limit may have a different purpose. In order to show that a certain assumption is wrong about properties common to all numbers of a particular form, the infinite descent proceeds to show that the number forming the limit (that is, the smallest possible number of that form) will appear to be dispossessed of certain properties which in fact it may be clearly seen to possess.

Fermat himself described this process in connection with his proof that every prime number of the form $(4n + 1)$ is composed of two squares. He first arbitrarily chose a particular prime and assumed that it was not the sum of two squares. He then proved (though he did not leave us his proof) that there must be another, less than the one chosen, and still another less than that, and so on. By infinite descent we finally reach the number 5, the smallest of all the numbers of this form $(4n + 1)$. By his proof, if the original assumption is correct then 5 cannot be represented as the sum of two squares. But it can, since

$$5 = 1^2 + 2^2$$

Consequently by a *reductio ad absurdum* we may infer that all prime numbers of the form $(4n + 1)$ may be represented as sums of two squares.

This method is useful in number theory, when it may be

appropriately applied, but it is not an easy matter to show the essential requirement that there must necessarily be a lesser number with the same relevant properties as some greater arbitrarily chosen number. For this reason, it is not often encountered.

The indirect method has a particular appeal to the intellect since it tackles a seemingly impossible task with consummate ease. This pleasure may appear somewhat perverse and the method has in fact encountered a certain amount of opposition from time to time. The objections are mainly along broadly ethical lines. Throughout our demonstrations we must live with a lie and not with a truth until such time as the destruction of the former establishes the validity of the latter.

To the strict logician the method of attack is underhand and something short of respectable. It smacks too much, for them, of irony, and this affords a less serious approach to mathematics. Stephen Leacock facetiously echoed the type of argument used in his own brand of 'boarding-house geometry' to prove that the bills of all boarders were 'equal each to each. For if not,' he says, 'let one bill be the greater; then the other bill is less than it might have been – which is absurd!'

Nevertheless the efficiency of the indirect method cannot be faulted any more than can the direct method, and if we have no other way of establishing our propositions then it would be foolish to reject the only method we do have. It should be noted here, however, that one school of mathematical thought rejects indirect proof as a logical non-starter in applications to the mathematics of the infinite. This is discussed in subsequent chapters.

It is of course sometimes possible to re-phrase an indirect proof so that a proposition may be given a direct proof. To prove that the number of primes is infinite, for example, we could instead of taking p as the greatest possible prime (as we did earlier in the chapter) take p as *any* prime.

We again form the number $(N + 1)$ where N is the product of all the primes less than and including p.

The number $(N + 1)$ is either itself prime or, if it is not a prime, it will have a factor which we shall call s. If $(N + 1)$ is divided by any of the primes whose product is N it will leave a remainder of 1. But s divides $(N + 1)$ without remainder.

Therefore s is not one of the primes less than and including p; and so for any given prime we can always find yet another greater prime. Consequently the number of primes must be infinite.

This proof does not have to expose any false assumption and is admittedly much more straightforward.

A quite different method of proof is that known as mathematical induction, which must at once be carefully distinguished from ordinary induction. There is no logical connection between the two processes. Mathematical induction commences in much the same way as induction by noting some examples of a particular result. It achieves its respectability, however, by showing a relationship between these results and then proving that this is necessarily a general relationship.

For example, we may establish a particular result for a quantity n and show that it also holds for the quantity $(n + 1)$. If n be *any* quantity, then this step enables us to show with great economy that the same result will hold for the quantities $(n + 2)$, $(n + 3)$ and so on.

This method is used for demonstrating that the expression $(x^n - 1)$ is divisible by $(x - 1)$ for all positive integral values of n. This would appear to involve a huge task, for the number of such values is, of course, infinite. Yet it is all very simple indeed. The secret, as was indicated above, is to establish a link between all these numbers in such a way that by showing that it is true of some numbers then it *must* be true for all of them.

By division

$$\frac{x^n - 1}{x - 1} = x^{n-1} + \frac{x^{n-1} - 1}{x - 1}$$

Consequently if $(x^{n-1} - 1)$ is divisible by $(x - 1)$ so that the second term on the right-hand side of the equation is an integer, then also must $(x^n - 1)$ be exactly divisible by $(x - 1)$.

We now take the simplest forms of $(x^{n-1} - 1)$ and note first that when $(n - 1) = 2$:

$$x^2 - 1 = (x - 1)(x + 1)$$

so that $(x^2 - 1)$ is divisible by $(x - 1)$. Therefore, by the above argument $(x^n - 1)$ or, in this particular instance, $(x^3 - 1)$ must also be divisible by $(x - 1)$. This establishes the necessary link for if $(x^3 - 1)$ is divisible by $(x - 1)$ then so must $(x^{3+1} - 1)$ or $(x^4 - 1)$ be similarly divisible. This is clearly a continuous process. Consequently we may assert at once that $(x^{100} - 1)$ is divisible by $(x - 1)$ without having to work through the actual division – which is just as well or we would never get to Chapter 3.

It will have been observed from the foregoing that different kinds of method are called to our aid for the differing requirements of particular types of proof. It is often possible to use short cuts or to effect substitutions and transformations of expressions and equations to make the task of proof simpler. A great deal of ingenuity has been employed in the development of such devices; these and other specific proofs will make their appearances in their appropriate places in later pages.

Meanwhile some amusement may be afforded by attempting an arithmetic restoration, a problem which although presented in the guise of a pastime, nevertheless calls for its fair share of ingenuity and logic. The solution depends upon the properties of numbers themselves, but it also depends upon acute observation. A typical problem provides the framework of some calculation from which most of the digits have been removed. The object is to restore the digits so as to reveal the calculation in its entirety.

$$
\begin{array}{r}
\ldots)\ldots\ldots\ldots(.7\ldots \\
\ldots \\
\hline
\ldots \\
\ldots \\
\hline
\ldots \\
\ldots \\
\hline
\ldots \\
\ldots \\
\hline
\end{array}
$$

The example above looks practically hopeless. A preliminary problem is to know where to start. The solution, however, is much less difficult than it would appear.

The first point to note is that the divisor is a factor of the dividend since there is no remainder. A more significant observation, however, reveals that although there are five digits in the quotient, only four divisions were effected. One of the digits in the quotient must therefore be 0 and we can identify it by noting where it is necessary to bring down two digits from the dividend at one time. This occurs when two digits are brought down for the purpose of the last division. This division provides the last digit in the quotient. Accordingly the digit immediately before this (that is, the fourth digit in the quotient) is 0.

It may next be observed that the third digit in the quotient is greater than the second digit (that is, greater than 7) since the multiplication of the divisor by the former gives a number which, when deducted from a *four-digit* number, leaves a remainder having only *two digits*; whereas multiplication of the divisor by 7 gives a product which still leaves a *three-digit* remainder when deducted from a *three-digit* number.

The third digit in the quotient is thus either 8 or 9. But again, the first and last digits in the quotient must each be greater than the third digit because they each give a four-figure product when multiplying the divisor, whereas the third digit in the quotient gives only a three-figure product. If the third digit in the quotient is 9, there can be no greater digit; accordingly the third digit in the quotient is 8 and the first and last digits are each 9.

The quotient thus stands revealed as 97,809. This much has been discovered without any idea whatever as to the magnitude of the divisor or of the dividend. Nevertheless these may be identified in one move, there being no need to search for each digit individually.

When the divisor is multiplied by 8 (the third digit in the quotient), the product is not greater than 999 since this product has only three digits. Consequently the divisor cannot be greater than 124.

From this it follows that the product resulting from the multiplication of the divisor (which cannot exceed 124) by 9 (the last digit of the quotient) cannot be greater than 1,116. In particular the first two digits of this product cannot form a number greater than 11, this being the remainder resulting from the previous division.

Now the product resulting from the multiplication of the divisor by 8 (the third digit of the quotient) which when deducted from a four-digit number (which must be at least 1,000) leaves a remainder not greater than 11, must itself be not less than 989. The divisor must therefore be greater than 123 since 123 × 8 gives a product of 984 and the product is required to be at least 989.

We have thus established that the divisor must be greater than 123 but not greater than 124. It must therefore be 124. The dividend is then simply obtained by multiplying the quotient by the divisor, giving the main items of the calculation as

$$124)\ 12,128,316\ (97,809$$

The remaining digits in the structure can then all be supplied by working through the process of division.

This solution is unique. The method employed is not at all what might have been intuitively anticipated as being the appropriate one to use, and it demonstrates that there must be a flexibility of approach to mathematical problems and proofs.

3. Triangle Everlasting

The Theorem of Pythagoras is remarkable as being the one theorem of which everybody has heard but of which they just happen for the moment to have forgotten the proof!

Of all the propositions in Euclidean geometry this was the revelation which appeared to the Pythagoreans to accord most with the fundamentals of the eternal harmony of existence. No doubt they chanted its purport with due solemnity in their mystic psalms:

> The Square on the Hypotenuse,
> Of a Right-angled Triangle
> Is Equal to the Sum
> Of the Squares
> On the other two Sides.

The rhythm and suggested intonation, in the English version at least, is unmistakable. Presumably hallowed by the more lowly and certainly less solemn chanting in centuries of geometry classes, it still retains its suggestive measure of poetic inevitability.

It is fashionable to doubt whether Pythagoras himself discovered the theorem at all. As with all our cherished beliefs, the authority for his personal contribution has suffered the attrition of time. The longer a tradition has existed, so the greater the scope and the louder the voice of doubt.

Pythagoras headed a sect of philosophy which, in addition to the more serious rules as to mathematical secrecy, imposed upon its members certain rather more grotesque prohibitions such as forbidding them to eat beans, or to sit on quart measures – surely an easy taboo to avoid. The sect appear to have conducted their affairs along such democratic principles that the leader rejoiced in the credit for all their discoveries. This revised 'tradition' is as much supposition as was the original. No matter what the truth of it may be, the truth of the theorem remains for all to see.

It is in many ways an astonishing theorem in that its apparent simplicity has many unexpected manifestations and ramifications. It lurks almost everywhere in Euclidean geometry. Scratch but a little way into a geometrical problem and there, like Emerson's blazing ubiquities, more likely than not will stand revealed the glittering generalities of the right-angled triangle.

The theorem is even more remarkable for the multiplicity of proofs by which it may be demonstrated. There are, indeed, more than three hundred and fifty different proofs and demonstrations, some of them it is true being variants of each other – a different demonstration for every day of the year! Here is an excellent example of the many ways in which certain problems may be attacked as well as of the many different applications to which a single principle may be relevant.

The origin of an awareness of the properties of some specific right-angled triangles lies well before the Greeks established a general proof. The Egyptians were well aware that the angle between the shorter sides of a triangle, whose sides measured 3, 4, and 5 units respectively, was a right angle – or perhaps was sufficiently close to what they may have called a 'square corner angle' since this would indicate the uses for which they would have needed to form such an angle.

It may not have occurred to them that the triangle thus formed was a particular example of a general type, although archaeologists have discovered a tablet upon which some member of the ancient Babylonian culture had listed fifteen triplets of numbers representing the dimensions of other specific triangles. It seems that the Babylonians were well acquainted with the general basic idea, although they could have built up their list of fifteen triplets out of a tedious trial and error process. Other early examples of the theorem have been found in China and other Asiatic countries and, although the dating of these finds is a matter of archaeological conjecture, they were certainly before Pythagoras's time.

The Egyptians used a rope for marking out right-angled

triangles. For the triangle with sides of 3, 4, and 5 units respectively they selected a piece of rope which was divided by knots into 12 segments of equal length.

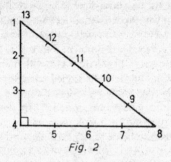

Fig. 2

They then selected a base line from which the triangle was to be measured. The part of the rope between the 4th and the 8th knots (assuming that a knot was also tied at each end of the rope)

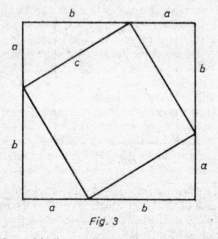

Fig. 3

was laid along this line, pulled taut and then pegged down at these two extreme knots. The two ends of the rope were then pulled together and, the rope having been tautened, a third stake was placed where the two ends of the rope met. (Fig. 2)

There is an especial neatness about the dimensions of this particular triangle. The lengths of the sides are represented by the three consecutive integers 3, 4, and 5; and the consecutive integers from 1 to 13 may be spaced at equal distances along its perimeter. This must have had a particular appeal for the Pythagoreans who attributed specific qualities to integers. Their eventual discovery that the property observed in the numbers 3, 4, and 5 was but a special case of a particular form of general number combination must have seemed to them the veritable vision of truth. The Egyptians built their pyramids with the help of the right-angled triangle; the Greeks tried to make it the cornerstone of the universe.

It has been suggested that Pythagoras may have discovered the essence of the theorem while idly observing the pattern of a tiled pavement. Whether this is true or not, it is certainly true that the idea could have been suggested to him in this way. Some interesting composition patterns may be used to demonstrate the theorem.

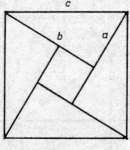

Fig. 4

In Fig. 3 is a square of side $(a + b)$ with an inscribed square of side c. The area of the larger square is equal to the sum of the area of the smaller square and the total area of the four triangles, the area of each of which is $\frac{1}{2}ab$. That is

$$(a + b)^2 = 4(\tfrac{1}{2}ab) + c^2$$

so $$a^2 + 2ab + b^2 = 2ab + c^2$$

or $$a^2 + b^2 = c^2$$

In view of the immense importance of the relationship between the sides of a right-angled triangle, the simplicity of the above demonstration is nothing less than astonishing.

An ingenious adaptation of the construction in Fig. 3 provides an intriguing alternative demonstration (Fig. 4). For this we cut out the four triangles *abc* and rearrange these *within* the square of side *c*, incidentally also forming a smaller square of side $(a - b)$ between the triangles. The area of the larger square is equal to the sum of the areas of the four triangles and the area of the smaller square. That is

$$c^2 = 4(\tfrac{1}{2}ab) + (a - b)^2$$

or

$$c^2 = 2ab + a^2 - 2ab + b^2$$

and

$$c^2 = a^2 + b^2$$

A quite different kind of dissection and fitting-together exercise may be carried out as in Fig. 5.

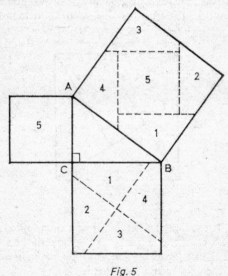

Fig. 5

The dotted lines in the square on side CB are drawn through the midpoint of the square; they are drawn parallel and perpendicular respectively to the hypotenuse AB. The square is thus divided into four congruent quadrilaterals marked with the identifying numbers 1 to 4. These together with the square on side AC (identified by the number 5) will fit exactly into the square on the hypotenuse.

The simplest proof based upon the use of similar triangles requires very little construction. In the right-angled triangle in Fig. 6, the line AD is perpendicular to the hypotenuse BC.

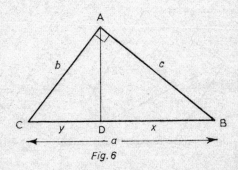

Fig. 6

Two triangles are similar if two angles of one are equal to two angles of the other, each to each; and the property of similar triangles which we shall use here is that the corresponding sides of the two triangles are proportional.

The triangles ADB and CAB are similar because they each contain the angle B as well as a right angle. So the side BD is to the side AB as the side AB is to BC, that is

$$\frac{x}{c} = \frac{c}{a} \text{ whence } x = \frac{c^2}{a}$$

Also the triangles CDA and CAB are similar because they each contain the angle C and a right angle, so

$$\frac{y}{b} = \frac{b}{a} \text{ whence } y = \frac{b^2}{a}$$

But $x + y = a$ by construction.

Substituting the values derived for x and y, this equation becomes

$$\frac{c^2}{a} + \frac{b^2}{a} = a$$

whence $\qquad\qquad c^2 + b^2 = a^2$

Euclid's proof of the theorem employs the concept of equal areas. The triangle in Fig. 7 has angle $CAB = 90°$.

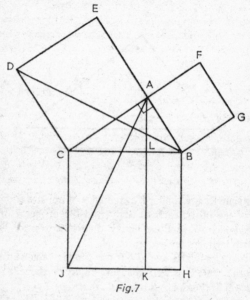

Fig. 7

Squares are constructed on the respective sides of the triangle as shown. The points A J are joined, as also are the points B D. Line AK is drawn parallel to BH. It is first proved that BA and AE are segments of the same line (that is BAE is a straight line) since the adjacent angles BAC and EAC are both right angles. For similar reasons CAF is also a straight line.

It is then shown that the area of triangle DBC is equal to the area of triangle AJC, these being equal triangles (by Euclid's fourth proposition) because the sides $DC = AC$; $CB = CJ$; and the included angles $DCB = ACJ$.

But the area of triangle DBC is equal to half the area of square AD, being on the same base DC, and between the same parallel lines DC and EB.

Again the area of triangle AJC is equal to half the area of rectangle JL, being on the same base JC, and between the same parallel lines JC and KA.

Since the areas of these two triangles are equal, then the area of square AD is equal to the area of rectangle JL.

Similarly, by joining CG, and joining AH, the same type of argument shows that the area of square AG is equal to the area of the rectangle HL. The two rectangles JL and HL together form the square CH. Thus:

$$\left.\begin{array}{l} \text{Area AD } (= AC^2) = \text{Area JL} \\ \text{Area AG } (= AB^2) = \text{Area HL} \end{array}\right\} = \text{Area CH } (= BC^2)$$

$$\text{Adding: } AC^2 + AB^2 \qquad\qquad = \qquad\qquad BC^2$$

Pythagoras is supposed to have been so elated at his discovery of the theorem that he forthwith indulged his favourite sport of sacrificing a hecatomb (one hundred oxen). Where he always managed to find so many oxen is something of a mystery, and anyone who has suffered the surfeit of turkey sandwiches after Christmas will realize how embarrassing the whole affair would have been. Proclus indeed says that only one ox was sacrificed; and Cicero throws cold water on the whole idea by pointing out that the Pythagoreans were reputedly vegetarians, implying that the sight of so much red meat would have put them off their nuts for at least a month.

In any case, however, the joy was to be short-lived. For in the very theorem which was thought to establish the supremacy of whole numbers in a numerical universe, the Pythagoreans were dismayed to find there lurked disturbing and startling evidence which threatened the very foundation of their beliefs.

The theorem applies equally to any right-angled triangle; but when they studied the special properties of an isosceles right-angled triangle, they discovered to their horror that the hypotenuse could not be measured by their kind of number at all. Again, the theorem holds good whether the sides are represented by whole numbers or by fractions, though Pythagoras was particularly interested in whole numbers; but it was found that other numbers which were neither whole nor fractional were involved. These were numbers whose existence had never even been suspected and there were infinitely many others.

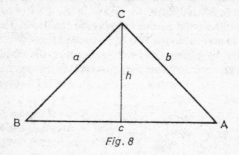

Fig. 8

In Fig. 8, the triangle ABC is isosceles with a right angle at C. Consequently

$$a^2 + b^2 = c^2$$

But $$a = b$$

So $$2a^2 = c^2$$

If we try to find values of a and c such that both are whole numbers, we shall be doomed to disappointment. It is impossible that the square of any whole number can be exactly twice as great as the square of any other whole number. From the above equation,

$$c = a\sqrt{2}$$

In the particular case where $a = 1$; so $c = \sqrt{2}$. But whatever the integral value of a, the value of c will always be a multiple of $\sqrt{2}$. This is an irrational, or incommensurable, number. It cannot be expressed as a fraction (or ratio) and its decimal equivalent does not terminate or recur; it cannot be measured against any scale which is marked off with rational numbers.

It has been suggested that Pythagoras sacrificed yet another hecatomb at this startling discovery, presumably in a bittersweet mood of sorrowful celebration, although it might seem to have been more reasonable to have asked for his other hundred back. To these philosophers the discovery was as disastrous as it was possible to be and was certainly not included among what W. S. Gilbert later referred to as the many 'cheerful facts about the square of the hypotenuse'.

It threatened their whole concept of proportion which was at the basis of much of their mathematical thinking. How could they speak of proportional relationships between the sides of a triangle if one or more of the sides could not even be measured?

Eventually they managed to live with irrationals if not to love them. But the whole matter was treated at first as a dreadful secret and they called the irrational 'alogon' or 'unutterable'. One can see their point of view. Strict secrecy was enjoined upon the fraternity, but legend relates that a certain Hippasus who, like the unfortunate barber of Midas, could not keep so sensational a secret to himself, revealed the irrational crisis to the vulgar laity. He met a sudden death by drowning in a convenient shipwreck in circumstances which were something of a mystery except to Proclus who wrote: '. . . the unutterable and the formless must needs be concealed. And those who uncovered and touched this image of life were instantly destroyed and shall remain for ever exposed to the play of the eternal waves.'

Since the number representing the hypotenuse in an isosceles right-angled triangle is incommensurable, there arises an apparent paradox in that we can draw the hypotenuse and yet not measure it or, alternatively, since we cannot measure it then we can *not* draw it. This seeming contradiction derives, however, from the notion that we can draw lines of rational length whereas in fact we cannot do this either. The imperfection of the surfaces available to us on which to draw and the experimental error which enters into all physical measurements make this impossible. The real difference between rational and irrational quantities is that we could measure the former if we could exclude the experimental error; that is, the rational quantities theoretically have an identifiable measurable quality irrespective of our inability to measure it. Irrational quantities do not have this same inherent quality; they would never be measurable in any circumstances of measure perfection.

An amusing fallacy is based on this predicament. The area of the triangle in Fig. 8 is equal to half the product of c (the base) and h (the height). That is

$$\text{area} = \tfrac{1}{2}ch$$

Now c is also the hypotenuse and irrational. Therefore, it seems, the area of the triangle is also incommensurable. What can this mean?

If we now construct another right-angled triangle ADB on AB as in Fig. 9 so that this triangle is equal in all respects to triangle ACB, then ADBC is a square of side a. Its area is a^2 and the area of triangle is thus $\tfrac{1}{2}a^2$ – which is commensurable. Thus this area is both commensurable and incommensurable!

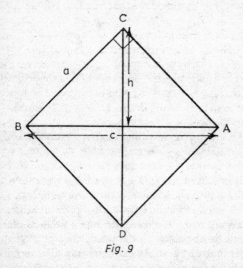

Fig. 9

The fallacy lies in the assumption that the quantity $\tfrac{1}{2}ch$ is irrational because c is irrational. In fact, however, inspection of the diagram shows that $h = \tfrac{1}{2}c$ since c is a diagonal of the square and h is half the other diagonal. Thus h is itself irrational and the area of triangle is

$$\frac{ch}{2} = \frac{c}{2}(h) = \left(\frac{\sqrt{(2a^2)}}{2}\right)\left(\frac{\sqrt{(2a^2)}}{2}\right) = \frac{a^2}{2}$$

This fallacy has a useful purpose in showing that the products of irrational quantities will sometimes be rational because of the cancelling out of the irrationals.

The proof, due to Euclid, that $\sqrt{2}$ is irrational is regarded as a gem for the ease with which it achieves its purpose. If such a root were rational then it could be represented as

$$\frac{a}{b}$$

where the latter fraction is in its lowest terms – that is, a and b have no common factors. Then either a or b, or both, must be odd; for if a and b are both even, they would have the common factor 2. If

$$\frac{a}{b} = \sqrt{2} \qquad \text{then} \frac{a^2}{b^2} = 2$$
$$\text{and } a^2 = 2b^2$$

Thus a^2, and therefore also a, is even. We can then represent a as $2m$.

Then	$a^2 = 4m^2$
but	$a^2 = 2b^2$
so	$2b^2 = 4m^2$
and	$b^2 = 2m^2$

whence b^2, and therefore also b, is even. Thus both a and b are even so that the fraction is *not* in its lowest terms. This contradicts the original assumption that it is in its lowest terms; as Aristotle expresses it: 'the same number is both even and odd' which is clearly impossible.

The development of geometry flourished to a much greater extent than did arithmetic in the hands of the Greeks for, although they were passionately interested in numbers, they had no satisfactory notation in which to express them. Instead they expressed themselves in geometry which was not so much a matter of lines and angles as a means of expressing in material form the abstract concept of number.

The number relationships evident in the relative dimensions of the respective sides of right-angled triangles can, of course, also be expressed algebraically with much greater economy and generality. It is possible to derive formulae which will generate all the sets of Pythagorean number triplets and to demonstrate through them number relationships which have no apparent direct connection with right-angled triangles.

The following identity holds for all values of m:

$$m^2 + \left(\frac{m^2 - 1}{2}\right)^2 = \left(\frac{m^2 + 1}{2}\right)^2$$

If m is odd, each of these terms is a whole number; if m is even, m^2 is also even, and the other terms will be fractions. When $m = 3$, the equation becomes the familiar

$$3^2 + 4^2 = 5^2$$

Another identity:

$$(m^2 - n^2)^2 + (2mn)^2 = (m^2 + n^2)^2$$

has terms which are always whole numbers for all positive integral values of m and n whether odd or even. When $m = 2$, $n = 1$; the equation becomes

$$(2^2 - 1^2)^2 + (2.2.1)^2 = (2^2 + 1^2)^2$$
or $$3^2 + 4^2 \qquad = 5^2$$

Yet another identity may be used which gives whole number values when $2ab$ is a perfect square:

$$(a + \sqrt{(2ab)})^2 + (b + \sqrt{(2ab)})^2 = (a + b + \sqrt{(2ab)})^2$$

when $a = 1$; $b = 2$; then

$$(1 + \sqrt{4})^2 + (2 + \sqrt{4})^2 = (1 + 2 + \sqrt{4})^2$$
or $$3^2 + 4^2 \qquad = 5^2$$

These three equations are built up from quite different number relationships. It is intriguing to note these examples of different ways in which integers can be associated so as to generate sets of Pythagorean number triplets.

There are also some very interesting properties in every set of Pythagorean numbers. In any triplet, one number is always a multiple of 3 and another is always a multiple of 5; the product of the two smaller numbers is always a multiple of 12, and the product of all three numbers is always a multiple of 60.

One particular problem which greatly exercised the minds of mathematicians, until Fermat set to work on it, was to identify a right-angled triangle whose sides are represented by whole numbers and whose area is equal to a perfect square. Fermat used his method of infinite descent to prove that this was impossible.

It is perhaps not so widely appreciated that the area relationship between figures constructed on the sides of right-angled triangles is not restricted to squares. There is a more general relationship for figures which are similar to each other.

In Fig. 10, for example, the area of the semi-circle on the hypotenuse is equal to the sum of the areas of the other two semi-circles.

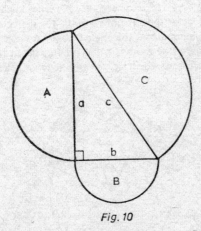

Fig. 10

Since all semi-circles are similar to each other their respective areas are proportional to the squares of their radii which, in Fig. 10, are in turn proportional to the sides of the triangle. That is

$$\frac{\text{Area A}}{\text{Area C}} = \frac{a^2}{c^2} \qquad \frac{\text{Area B}}{\text{Area C}} = \frac{b^2}{c^2}$$

But since, from the triangle, $a^2 + b^2 = c^2$; then, dividing by c^2,

$$\frac{a^2}{c^2} + \frac{b^2}{c^2} = \frac{1}{1}$$

and substituting the area relationships

$$\frac{\text{Area A}}{\text{Area C}} + \frac{\text{Area B}}{\text{Area C}} = 1$$

so
$$\text{Area A} + \text{Area B} = \text{Area C}$$

The same principles apply to other similar figures. The reader may find it an interesting pastime to discover the variety of possibilities and the surprising patterns which emerge.

The general principle of the Pythagoras Theorem may be applied to any problem in which it is possible to introduce the properties of a right-angled triangle into the calculation.

It may, for example, be used in connection with problems concerning circles by virtue of certain properties such as that the angle subtended at the circumference by the diameter of a circle is a right angle, as also is the angle between a tangent to a circle at any point and the radius at that point. Thus it is possible to measure dimensions which we cannot otherwise reach.

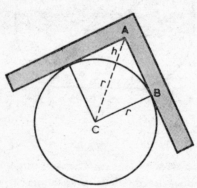

Fig. 11

The bore of a pipe may be measured with the help of a carpenter's square (see Fig. 11). The triangle ABC is an isosceles right-angled triangle of which the hypotenuse AC is equal to

$(r + h)$ and, by Pythagoras' Theorem, is also equal to $\sqrt{(2r^2)} = r\sqrt{2}$.

Thus $\qquad r + h = r\sqrt{2}$

so $\qquad\qquad h = r(\sqrt{2} - 1)$

and $\qquad\qquad r = \left(\dfrac{1}{\sqrt{2} - 1}\right) h = 2\cdot414h$ (approx.)

So by measuring the distance h *outside* the pipe we can calculate the length of the radius. The diameter of the pipe is twice as great as its radius, and the bore of the pipe can then be deduced by allowing for the thickness of the metal or other material.

The intimate nature of the relationship between the circle and the right-angled triangle is perfectly illustrated by means of analytic or co-ordinate geometry, which itself embodies the remarkable affinity between algebra and geometry. The essence of this system is that any point in a plane may be defined by reference to its position relative to co-ordinate axes. Every equation has its curve and every curve has its equation. Algebraic equations may be solved by reference to the properties of their curves; the properties of curves may be deduced algebraically or by means of the calculus.

In Fig. 12, a quadrant of a circle has been drawn

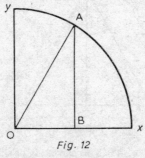

Fig. 12

with its centre at O, the origin of a system of co-ordinate axes. A is any point represented by a number pair x,y. OA is the radius at A. That is: BA $= y$; OB $= x$; OA $= r$. By Pythagoras theorem

$$r^2 = x^2 + y^2$$

and this equation which relates the dimensions of the triangle is also the equation of this circle. In this quadrant where all the values are positive

$$y = \sqrt{(r^2 - x^2)}$$

As point A is made to move towards the x axis so y decreases as x increases, but this change always occurs in such a way that the above equation always holds for every point on the circle in the quadrant. An infinite number of right-angled triangles may theoretically be constructed within the quadrant in this way. In each triangle the hypotenuse is equal to r, the radius, whereas the lengths of the other two sides vary as noted above.

For a given hypotenuse length, the dimensions of the right-angled triangles which can be constructed on that hypotenuse are restricted to those of the triangles which can be drawn within the circle.

One particular right-angled triangle which is of special use and interest is the triangle with angles of 30, 60, and 90 degrees respectively. In this, the length of the shorter side is exactly half the length of the hypotenuse. In Fig. 13, ABC is such a triangle.

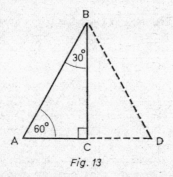

Fig. 13

AC is half the length of AB. This can easily be shown by drawing the triangle DBC so that it is equal in all respects to triangle ABC. This effectively forms the equilateral triangle ABD. Then AB = AD. But AC = $\frac{1}{2}$AD. So also AC = $\frac{1}{2}$AB.

If then AB = 1; so AC = 0·5; and by Pythagoras theorem, BC = $\sqrt{(1^2 - (0·5)^2)}$ = 0·866. These values may now be used to illustrate the link between Pythagoras' theorem and trigonometry; for although trigonometry has expanded well beyond its humble beginnings it nevertheless found these in the properties of right-angled triangles.

Trigonometrical ratios relative to respective angles are calculated as ratios between the dimensions of the sides of the triangle. The three basic ratios – sine, cosine and tangent – of angle ABC (= 30°) in Fig. 13 are calculated from the dimensions of the triangle sides shown above thus:

$$\sin 30° = \frac{\text{opposite side (AC)}}{\text{hypotenuse (AB)}} = \frac{0\cdot 5}{1} = 0\cdot 5 \text{ (exactly)}$$

$$\cos 30° = \frac{\text{adjacent side (BC)}}{\text{hypotenuse (AB)}} = \frac{0\cdot 886}{1} = 0\cdot 886 \text{ (approx.)}$$

$$\tan 30° = \frac{\text{opposite side (AC)}}{\text{adjacent side (BC)}} = \frac{0\cdot 5}{0\cdot 886} = 0\cdot 5744 \text{ (approx.)}$$

Trigonometrical ratios for angles of other magnitudes are calculated in exactly the same way from the dimensions of triangles containing the angles. There is a unique value of each ratio for each magnitude of angle. Thus

$$\sin 28° = 0\cdot 4695$$
$$\sin 29° = 0\cdot 4848$$
$$\sin 30° = 0\cdot 5$$
$$\sin 31° = 0\cdot 5150 \text{ (approx.)}$$

These values are of course numbers. Thus we have the properties of triangles expressed in number form. Conversely, it is possible, by employing trigonometrical relationships, to perform purely arithmetical calculations which in themselves have nothing to do with right angles.

One particular relationship (the proof of which will be found in elementary trigonometry textbooks) is embodied in the identity

$$\sin A . \cos B = \tfrac{1}{2} [\sin (A + B) + \sin (A - B)]$$

This effectively converts the process of multiplication into one of addition, just as may be done by the use of logarithms although the principles involved are quite different.

The equation is expressed in trigonometrical terms. For the special case when A = 25°; B = 21°; the equation becomes

$$\sin 25° \cos 21° = \tfrac{1}{2} [\sin 46° + \sin 4°] \ldots\ldots \quad \text{(i)}$$

Substituting the relevant numerical values (from tables) gives

$$(0\cdot4226) (0\cdot9336) = \tfrac{1}{2} [0\cdot7193 + 0\cdot0698] = 0\cdot3945$$

the result being correct to four decimal places.

The last form in which the equation appears is entirely numerical. If it is desired to multiply 0·4226 by 0·9336, we merely ascertain the angles of which these are the sine and cosine values respectively. This enables us to construct an equation similar to that in (i) above, and the next step is to note the values of the sines (again from tables) of the two angles which appear on the right-hand side of the equation. Half the sum of these two values then gives the desired answer.

The theorem of Pythagoras may indeed appear in many guises. A few have been noted here; others will occur in later pages. On a lighter note, there is the story of a tall mathematician whose prospective landlady doubted whether she could provide a bed which was long enough for him. He is said to have laid his walking-stick once across the bed and twice along its length and then to have declared: 'I shall sleep diagonally!'

4. The Root of the Matter

Although the square of every whole number is itself also a whole number, the converse is not true. This is at once apparent since only those numbers which are perfect squares can have square roots which are whole numbers. Nevertheless, within the structural neatness such as is expected of mathematics, it is still possible to share Pythagoras's surprise – if not his dismay – that all other square roots of whole numbers are not merely not whole numbers but that they cannot be expressed in a finite number of digits or decimals at all.

These comprise part of the class of irrational numbers (there are others) and Pythagoras would have been only too willing to have been able to excommunicate them. More modern commentators have also expressed similar doubts as to the propriety of admitting them to the hierarchy of numbers. But this is like trying to seal off a besieged town after it has been overrun – they are already in.

Perhaps the greatest interest in square roots arises from an appreciation of the multiplicity of diverse ways in which they may be calculated or estimated. Many people may be surprised that square roots can be interesting at all. At school the extraction of roots is almost as unpopular as it is in the dentist's chair. The operation itself is expressed in terms which suggest that brute force is required to make numbers yield the secrets of their roots. It is true that the labour of the actual calculations can scarcely be described as exciting, but the underlying principles and their connections with differing branches of mathematics are of great fundamental interest.

Where an approximation to only a few significant figures will suffice, the simplest method of extracting roots is by the use of logarithms. The logarithm of a number is twice the logarithm of its square root. The extraction of the root is thus converted into a simple division by 2.

Thus
$$\log 25 = 1·3979$$
$$\tfrac{1}{2} \log 25 = 0·6990$$
$$\text{Antilog } 0·6990 = 5 \qquad = \sqrt{25}$$

The value of roots can also be read off from slide-rules or from printed tables. This is more practical for actual working purposes, but a book of printed tables is to mathematics what the dictionary is to literature – indispensable for practical reference but entirely lacking in imagination.

The easiest way of extracting roots of perfect squares is by factorizing.

Thus
$$1521 = 13^2 \times 3^2$$
So
$$\sqrt{1521} = 13 \times 3 = 39$$

This method is also useful for simplifying the extraction of roots of numbers which are composite but are not perfect squares. instead of having to extract the root of 507 we may note that this number is equal to 3×13^2. Its root is therefore $13 \sqrt{3}$ and we only have to extract the root of 3.

Where there are no short cuts to exploit, the method which is taught resembles a form of division. For this reason it is sometimes confusing – it looks like an ordinary division but is not. It is most easily explained by an example – the extraction of the square root of 155,236.

The first step is to mark the number off into pairs of digits working away from the decimal point. This marking off is as shown in the first line of column *b* below. Subsequent steps are:

a	b			c	
3	15	52	36	394	
3	9				
69	6	52			...... (d)
9	6	21			
784		31	36		...... (e)
		31	36		

Find the greatest perfect square which is contained in the first pair of digits (15). This square is 9, the square root of which is 3. Place this digit (3) as the first digit in the answer (column c) and also in column a; and deduct its square (9) from the first pair of digits in column b. This leaves a remainder of 6; bring down the next pair of digits to form the number 652. Double the number in column a: ($2 \times 3 = 6$) and bring this down as the first digit of a number of which the unit digit (x) has yet to be determined, such that the number thus formed will divide into the number in column b: (652) x times and leave the smallest possible remainder under these conditions. Here it will be found that 69 will divide into 652 nine times, leaving a remainder of 31. Form the divisor accordingly and carry out a straightforward division, placing the digit 9 as the second digit in the answer.

Bring down the next pair of digits in column b to form the number 3,136. Add to the divisor formed above (69) a number equal to its unit digit (9) to form the number 78 and bring this down as before as the first two digits of the next divisor. It will then be found that the number 784 will divide into 3,136 exactly four times. Carry out this division, and place the digit 4 as the next and last digit in the answer. This gives 394 as the square root of 155,236.

This process may seem to be too mechanical to be of any lasting interest and the reasons for some of the steps taken are often not clearly visualized. The method may, however, be illuminated by a transformation to its geometrical analogue in which it probably originated.

It should, however, be observed first that the above method is a shorthand form of a fuller method. When we apparently subtracted 9 (that is 3^2) from 15 (the first pair of digits) we really subtracted 90,000 (or 300^2) from the original number 155,236, leaving a remainder of 65,236. The last two digits of this number are not brought down into line (d) as they are not required for our calculations at that stage.

Similarly, the number 3,136 in line (e) is equal to the difference between the original number 155,236 and the square of 390.

The reason for selecting the digit 3 as the first digit in the square root is that we know, by trial and error, that the square root of 155,236 lies between 300 and 400. Its first digit must therefore be 3. This and the subsequent steps are now shown geometrically.

In Fig. 14, ABCD is a square of area 155,236 square units. Finding the square root of 155,236 is then equivalent to calculating the length of the side of the square. The root lies between 300 and 400; that is, it is greater than 300. We therefore construct the square AEKH of side equal to 300 units inside the original square. HK is extended to F. EK is extended to G.

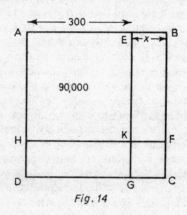

Fig. 14

The problem is thus changed once more into calculating the length EB, since AE + EB = AB. We already know the length of AE by construction. Let EB = x. Then the square root is 300 + x.

We have identified the first digit in the root as 3 and we proceed to identify the next digit. The area of AEKH is 90,000; the total area of the remainder of ABCD is thus 155,236 − 90,000 = 65,236. Here we reach a stage equivalent to that of line (d) in the arithmetical calculation. This remaining area consists of rectangles EBFK and HKGD, and the square FCGK. The area of this square is x^2; the area of each of the rectangles is 300x. Therefore, 2(300x) + x^2 = 65,236.

Since the area x^2 of the square FCGK is small compared with the total area of the two rectangles, we may ignore it to obtain an approximate value for x. Thus,

$$2(300x) \simeq 65,236$$

or
$$x \simeq 109$$

This value is clearly too great for x, since it would mean that $AB = 409$ and we know that in fact it lies between 300 and 400. At this stage we are looking only for a digit in the 'tens' position in the root so that for our approximation of the value of x we need a value which is a multiple of 10. It is shown above that x must not be much less than 109, but that it cannot be greater than 99. The next lowest multiple of 10 is 90 and we take this as an approximation for x.

Then AB is approximately $300 + 90 = 390$. The root is now known to lie between 390 and 400. This narrowing-down process continues for the identification of the digit in the unit position in the root.

We construct another square similar to that in Fig. 14 but, instead of making $AE = 300$, we make it 390. Let $EB = y$. The area of the square on AE is now 390^2 or $152,100$; so that the total area of the remaining rectangles and small square is $155,236 - 152,100 = 3,136$. Here we reach the same stage as in line (e) in the arithmetical calculation. The value of y may be estimated in the same way as the value of x was estimated.

$$2(390y) \simeq 3,136$$
$$y \simeq 4$$

and it is found by multiplying out that this is in fact the last digit required for the square root $= 394$.

If this had not given an exact result the process could have been continued to identify the first digit following the decimal point and so on. This geometric method would soon become tedious and would be too clumsy for calculating the values of irrational quantities to any given number of significant figures. The arithmetical calculation essentially follows the same basic principles but condenses the working into a more convenient method.

Another method which can best be demonstrated geometrically

in terms of area is the differential method. The diagram of the previous figure is repeated in Fig. 15 but the dimensions of the side segments are different. Here we use a notation which will become more familiar in the chapter on calculus.

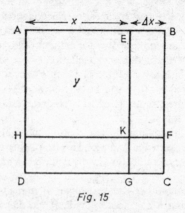

Fig. 15

The length of the side of the square on $AE = x$; the area of this square $= y = x^2$, all in suitable units of measurement. If each of the sides of the square is increased (for example, AE is increased to AB) by an increment represented by the symbol $\triangle x$ and a new square $ABCD$ is formed as shown, then the area within the square $AEKH$ will increase to the area of the square $ABCD$. Let this increment of area be represented by the symbol $\triangle y$, so that the area of $ABCD$ will be $y + \triangle y$.

Then the area $ABCD = (AE + EB)^2$

$$\text{or} \quad y + \triangle y = (x + \triangle x)^2$$
$$= x^2 + 2x\triangle x + (\triangle x)^2$$

but $y \qquad = x^2 \qquad\qquad$ (from square $AEKH$)

so $\qquad \triangle y = \qquad 2x\triangle x + (\triangle x)^2$ by subtraction

The last equation gives two terms on the right-hand side which are obtained by subtracting the equivalents (in x and $\triangle x$) of y from $y + \triangle y$. That is

$$(x + \triangle x)^2 - x^2 = 2x\triangle x + (\triangle x)^2$$

If $\triangle x$ is very small relative to x, then $(\triangle x)^2$ will be almost negligible in comparison. Thus if $\triangle x$ is as small as 0·001, then $(\triangle x)^2$ is only 0·000001. Consequently by ignoring $(\triangle x)^2$ altogether we shall be able to obtain an *approximate* solution which may well be as close as we need to an actual solution. Instead then of solving the above exact equation we solve the approximation

$$(x + \triangle x)^2 - x^2 \simeq 2x\triangle x$$

or
$$\triangle x \simeq \frac{(x + \triangle x)^2 - x^2}{2x} \quad \ldots\ldots \text{(i)}$$

This formula can be used with great effect in the approximation of irrational roots. At first glance it may seem to pose its own difficulty by including the unknown $\triangle x$ on both sides of the equation. However, if we set $(x + \triangle x)$ as the desired square root then the number whose root we are seeking will be $(x + \triangle x)^2$. While we do not know the value of $(x + \triangle x)$ we *do* know the value of $(x + \triangle x)^2$ and this value may be substituted at once into the equation. If we then assume a suitable value of x by inspection, then everything else follows very neatly.

To calculate the approximate value of the square root of 2, for example, we may first note that this root lies between 1 and 2 and that, as $\sqrt{1 \cdot 96}$ (which is very close to $\sqrt{2}$) is 1·4, this latter value can be taken as the value of x. That is

$$\sqrt{2} = (1 \cdot 4 + \triangle x)$$
and
$$2 = (1 \cdot 4 + \triangle x)^2$$

Substituting the value $x = 1 \cdot 4$; $(x + \triangle x)^2 = 2$ in approximation (i) gives

$$\triangle x \simeq \frac{2 - (1 \cdot 4)^2}{2(1 \cdot 4)} \text{ or } \mathbf{0 \cdot 014}$$

So
$$\sqrt{2} = x + \triangle x \simeq 1 \cdot 4 + 0 \cdot 014 \text{ or } \mathbf{1 \cdot 414}$$

This is a very close approximation since $(1 \cdot 414)^2 = 1 \cdot 999396$.

If an even closer approximation is required, the same process may be repeated by setting

$$\sqrt{2} = 1 \cdot 414 + \triangle x$$

and solving as before. This can be continued indefinitely to any required degree of accuracy, and is an example of a recursion formula.

The Greeks had an ingenious method, built upon two sequences of interrelated numbers, which they used to trap the value of $\sqrt{2}$. These sequences are in the form

Pair number	1	2	3	4	5	6	7	8	
Series a	1	3	7	17	41	99	239	577	etc.
Series b	1	2	5	12	29	70	169	508	

Each series begins with the number 1. Each term in series b is equal to the sum of the next previous number in that series and the relative number in the a series. Thus $2 = 1 + 1$; $5 = 2 + 3$; $12 = 5 + 7$ and so on. Each term in the a series is equal to the sum of its relative number in the b series and the next previous number in the b series. Thus, $3 = 2 + 1$; $7 = 5 + 2$; $17 = 12 + 5$ and so on.

The pairs of a and b numbers also conform to the rule that the first, third and, in general, all odd-numbered pairs are of the form $a^2 = 2b^2 - 1$; whereas the second, fourth and all even-numbered pairs are of the form $a^2 = 2b^2 + 1$.

Thus
$$7^2 = 2(5)^2 - 1$$
but
$$3^2 = 2(2)^2 + 1$$

The object of this build-up is to provide a sequence of values for the ratio a/b derived from successive pairs of numbers; the values thus obtained being alternately less than and greater than $\sqrt{2}$. The first few values are 1; 1·5; 1·4; 1·416.

Another method, which has echoes from the last method but which is instead built upon a recursion process, is based on the idea of taking the average of estimated values. It proceeds as follows. The value of $\sqrt{2}$ lies between 1 and 2; as an estimate we take its approximate value as 1·5 or 3/2. Divide this value into 2, giving the quotient 4/3. Take the average of 3/2 and 4/3, giving 17 ÷ 12 or 1·416. Again, divide this value into 2, giving the quotient 24/17 and take the average of 17/12 and 24/17; this average is $577 \div 408 = 1.414215$ – a very close approximation to $\sqrt{2}$ indeed.

The reason for this process will not be immediately apparent. However, if $\sqrt{x} = a$ exactly then also $x/a = a$. But if $\sqrt{x}$ is approximately equal to a, so that a is a close estimate but slightly too great, then x/a will be another estimate which is slightly too small. The average of a too-great estimate and a too-small estimate will give yet another approximation which is closer than either of the estimates which have been averaged. In general, if a is an estimate of $\sqrt{x}$, then the average of two estimates a and x/a will be

$$\left(a + \frac{x}{a}\right) \div 2 \quad or \quad \frac{a^2 + x}{2a}$$

This formula may be developed as follows. Let a be an approximation to the square root $(a + n)$ of the number x. That is $(a + n)^2 = x$. We note the identity

$$[(a + n) - a]^2 = (a + n)^2 - 2a(a + n) + a^2$$

If n be very small compared with a, we may neglect n^2 as being negligible. The left-hand side of the equation will then reduce to zero. At the same time, since $(a + n)^2 = x$, the right-hand side of the equation becomes simplified so that

$$0 \simeq x - 2a(a + n) + a^2$$

Whence, by transposing,

$$(a + n) \simeq \frac{a^2 + x}{2a}$$

It is of interest to note that the *averaged* ratios obtained in this method (for example $17 \div 12$; $577 \div 408$) all appear in the Greek series in the previous method. The present process, however, approaches the value of the root more rapidly – that is, it omits many of the ratios in the Greek series.

Yet another method for extracting roots is based upon the use of continued fractions. Any irrational root may be expressed as a continued fraction and its value calculated to any degree of accuracy from its successive convergents.

For example, if $x^2 = 2$, then also

$$x^2 - 1 = 1$$

or

$$(x - 1)(x + 1) = 1$$

so

$$(x - 1) = \frac{1}{1 + x}$$

and

$$x = 1 + \frac{1}{1 + x}$$

But x appears in the denominator of the fraction in this equation and can be replaced by $1 + 1/(1 + x)$ and this process can be continued indefinitely rather like the reflection of mirrors reflected in yet other mirrors. Thus we may obtain

$$\sqrt{2} = 1 + \cfrac{1}{2 + \cfrac{1}{2 + \cfrac{1}{2 + \dots}}}$$

The convergents will be found to be, in order,

$$\tfrac{3}{2} \quad \tfrac{7}{5} \quad \tfrac{17}{12} \quad \tfrac{41}{29}, \text{ etc.}$$

and these again are the same as the ratios from the Greek series!

It is also possible to obtain close approximations to correct values of roots from the expansion of the binomial $(1 + x)^n$. The first terms of the expansion are:

$$1 + nx + \frac{n(n - 1)}{1 \cdot 2} x^2 + \dots$$

If x is very small then, again, x^2 and higher powers of x are very much smaller in comparison and may be neglected. A reasonably approximate value for the expansion may in such circumstances be obtained from the first two terms. When n is fractional, the terms of the expansion are alternately positive and negative, but this does not affect the general principle here. The important requirement is that x shall be very small relative to 1.

To find the square root of 98, we may proceed as follows:

$$\sqrt{98} = \sqrt{(100 - 2)}$$
$$= \sqrt{(10^2 - 2)}$$
$$= 10^2\sqrt{(1 - 0.02)} \text{ or } 10(1 - 0.02)^{\frac{1}{2}}$$

This latter binomial is of the form $(1 + x)^n$ where $x = 0.02$ and $n = \frac{1}{2}$.

The approximate value is therefore

$$1 + nx = 1 - \tfrac{1}{2}(0.02)$$
$$= 1 - 0.01 \qquad = 0.99$$

and the approximate value of the square root is thus $10 \times 0.99 = 9.9$. This is close to the correct value since $(9.9)^2 = 98.01$.

The degree of accuracy depends upon the smallness of x, and the method itself depends upon our ability to express the original number in some form which includes the binomial $(1 + x)$.

Square roots can be represented geometrically in different ways. Perhaps the most familiar method is by means of the curve of $y = \sqrt{x}$, plotted from some known values, from which other required values may be read off. Very few people, however, have the ability to draw curves with a sufficient degree of accuracy.

Square roots can be 'constructed' by the use of Pythagoras' theorem into the intriguing shell-like diagram in Fig. 16.

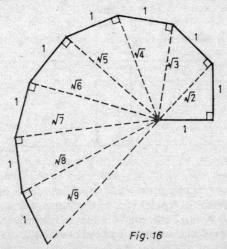

Fig. 16

We start with an isosceles right-angled triangle, the equal sides of which are each equal to 1 unit. The hypotenuse is then equal to $\sqrt{2}$. If we use this side as base and build on it another right-angled triangle of 1 unit height, the hypotenuse of this new triangle is $\sqrt{[(\sqrt{2})^2 + 1^2]} = \sqrt{3}$. A continuation of this same process will provide the square roots of all the natural numbers in succession.

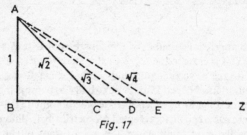

Fig. 17

Another method of achieving the same objective also begins with the properties of an isosceles right-angled triangle. In Fig. 17 the sides of triangle ABC are 1, 1, and $\sqrt{2}$ respectively. By marking off along BZ a length BD equal to AC and joining DA we construct a new triangle ABD in which the sides are 1, $\sqrt{2}$ and $\sqrt{3}$ respectively. Then a length BE (marked off along BZ) equal to DA will produce a triangle having sides of 1, $\sqrt{3}$ and $\sqrt{4}$ respectively, and so on.

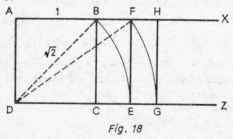

Fig. 18

A similar kind of method which reverses the above principle is shown in Fig. 18. ABCD is a square. Let $AB = 1$ unit. The diagonal DB then represents $\sqrt{2}$. With D as centre and this diagonal as radius, draw an arc cutting DZ at E. Thus $DE = \sqrt{2}$.

At E erect a perpendicular, cutting AX at F. The diagonal DF will now, by Pythagoras' theorem, represent $\sqrt{3}$. Again with D as centre and radius DF, draw an arc cutting DZ at G; and erect a perpendicular at G cutting AX at H. DH then represents $\sqrt{4}$. Successive roots may be represented by a continuation of the same method.

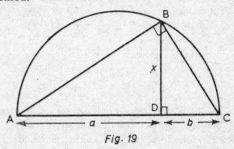

Fig. 19

A different method of construction to represent a given square root, without having to pass through all the intermediate construction, is based on the principle of the mean proportional. If a perpendicular is dropped on the hypotenuse of a right-angled triangle from the angle opposite (that is, the right angle itself) then this perpendicular will be the mean proportional between the two segments into which it divides the hypotenuse. That is to say, this proposition holds good (see Fig. 19):

$$\frac{a}{x} = \frac{x}{b}$$

To use this idea in connection with square roots, we equate a with the number whose root we wish to measure; and we equate b with 1. The above proportion then becomes

$$\frac{a}{x} = \frac{x}{1} \quad \text{or} \quad a = x^2$$
$$\text{whence } \sqrt{a} = x$$

We may thus measure the length of x to give us the value of $\sqrt{2}$.

The construction required for this is first to draw the line AC, and to draw a semi-circle with AC as diameter. The length of

AC will, of course, have been drawn as $(a + 1)$ with the point
D marking off the two separate segments. Erect a perpendicular
from D to cut the semi-circle at B; the length of this perpendicular
(x) represents $\sqrt{a}$.

A simpler construction may be achieved by drawing a right-
angled triangle of which the hypotenuse measures $(x + 1)$ units
and one of the sides measures $(x - 1)$ units. Then $\sqrt{x}$ will be
represented as half the length of the third side. This is based on
the identity

$$(x + 1)^2 = x^2 + 2x + 1$$
$$= x^2 - 2x + 1 + 4x$$

So $\qquad (x + 1)^2 = (x - 1)^2 + 4x$

This shows the square on the hypotenuse as the sum of the
square on one of the other sides plus the quantity $4x$. By Pythagoras' theorem therefore, $4x$ must represent the square on the
third side which must accordingly measure $\sqrt{(4x)}$ or $2\sqrt{x}$ units.
Therefore half the length of this side represents $\sqrt{x}$.

Values of roots obtained from constructions are, of course,
necessarily approximate because of the technical difficulties of
measurement. Much of this chapter has indeed been concerned
with approximation for the very simple reason that any value we
obtain for irrational roots can never be anything but an approximation, although the degree of accuracy can be made as fine as
we like.

The same compromise has to be made in other areas of mathematics. The generalized notion that the vaunted exactness of
mathematics must apply to each and every result, and that
approximations are for that reason not truly mathematics, is a
misconception. Exactness is a desirable virtue and is a matter for
insistence where it can be achieved; where it cannot be attained
we have to make do with sufficiently close approximations.
Something is always better than nothing at all, provided it is
something we want.

5. Sequence and Consequence

Reference was made in the previous chapter to sequences of interrelated integers which, taken in pairs, provide successively closer approximations to the value of $\sqrt{2}$. There is a good deal of fascination in sequences of this type, even when the constructions of the sequences are clearly visible.

Although the development of a sequence is the direct result of the human manipulation of numbers, the incidental properties which it generates within itself lie well beyond anything which could possibly have been envisaged beforehand. Indeed, so many examples have such unexpected significance that we can but pause in astonishment that numbers, which originated as a frame of reference for mere counting, should display such independence of spirit.

The manipulation of numbers may be thought to be trivial in itself, but the results may in fact be highly important, just as a good many mathematical discoveries with wide practical applications have originated in general number theory.

Perhaps the Fibonacci sequence is the most surprising sequence of all. For whereas most other sequences exhibit properties which lie strictly within the number system itself, the Fibonacci sequence, besides having peculiarities of its own, also appears to manifest itself in numbers associated directly with nature. It is associated with art through the medium of the golden section, offers a further interesting example of the mathematical concept of limits on which the calculus is based, and approximates remarkably closely to a natural rate of growth. Nor do we have to search very far for a connection between the sequence and Pythagoras theorem. An apparently mild numerical diversion proves to have significant links with many mathematical ideas.

The sequence is named after the Italian mathematician Leonardo of Pisa, who was better known by his patronymic Fibonacci. It first appeared in 1202 in his important work *Liber Abaci*. The first fourteen terms of the sequence are

1, 1, 2, 3, 5, 8, 13, 21, 34, 55, 89, 144, 233, 377, ...

each term, after the second, being the sum of the two next preceding terms. Thus $3 + 5 = 8$; $5 + 8 = 13$; and so on.

Fibonacci gave as an example the hypothetical breeding results of a colony of rabbits. If a pair of rabbits are placed in an enclosure, how many rabbits will be produced on the assumption that, starting in the second month after their birth, each pair of rabbits give birth to a further pair in each subsequent month?

The original pair will give birth to a new pair every month. Consequently by the end of the first month there will be *two* pairs. The original pair will again give birth in the second month, but the pair born in the first month will not. Thus at the end of the second month there will be three pairs. Of these, two pairs will each produce another pair in the third month, making a total then of *five* pairs; in the next month there will be three birth pairs, making a total of *eight* pairs. The numbers written in italics here are the same as in the Fibonacci sequence.

This is probably an unrealistic example based more on mathematical expediency than on rabbit psychology and, despite the rapid growth evidenced in the terms of the sequence, it largely understates the notorious habits and potential of these friendly white-scutted creatures. It is interesting, however, to note in passing that this notoriety has existed for at least 700 years; perhaps it has always been so.

A superficial glance at the terms of the sequence might suggest some difficulty in discovering general relationships and in establishing formulae for the sum of any number of terms or other like calculations. In fact, as a closer consideration will confirm, it is quite simple to demonstrate some of the basic relationships. Some examples now follow but, as it would be tedious to give proofs for all of them, we shall prove only one proposition and merely state the others. These may be checked experimentally and may afford the reader some mental diversion in attempting to establish proofs.

The sum of the first n terms in a Fibonacci sequence is given by a number which is 1 less than the $(n + 2)$th term. Thus the sum of the first five terms is 12:

$$1 + 1 + 2 + 3 + 5 = 12$$

and this is 1 less than the seventh term, 13. This may be demonstrated where U_1; U_2 etc. are the first, second and subsequent terms of the sequence; the subscripts indicating the positions of the terms in the series. Thus $U_1 = 1$; $U_4 = 3$; and so on.

We first have, by definition of the sequence:

$$U_1 + U_2 = U_3$$

So also

$$U_1 = U_3 - U_2$$

Similarly

$$U_2 = U_4 - U_3$$

$$U_3 = U_5 - U_4$$

$$\cdots\cdots$$

$$\cdots\cdots$$

In general

$$U_n = U_{n+2} - U_{n+1}$$

If all these equivalents are added, then the left-hand side will give the sum of all n terms; in the addition all except two of the terms on the right-hand side will cancel each other out to leave only

$$U_{n+2} - U_2$$

and as U_2 is 1, then the sum of the first n terms of the sequence is equal to

$$U_{n+2} - 1$$

The above example, where $U_2 = 1$, is a particular case of a general relationship for *any* Fibonacci-type sequence. In the sequence:

$$4, 7, 11, 18, 29 \ldots$$

we have:

$$U_1 = 4; \ U_2 = 7; \ U_n = 29; \ U_{n+2} = 76$$

and the sum of the series is:

$$U_{n+2} - U_2 = 76 - 7 = 69$$

The sum of *any* ten consecutive terms in a Fibonacci-type series is also exactly 11 times greater than the U_7th term. The sum of the ten terms

$$2, 3, 5, 8, 13, 21, 34, 55, 89, 144$$

is 374, which is equal to

$$11 \times 34 \ or \ 11(U_7)$$

and the tenth term itself is greater by $(U_2 - U_1)$ than 11 times U_5; that is:

$$(11 \times 13) + (3 - 2) = 144$$

The connection between the Fibonacci sequence and Pythagoras' theorem is established by the relationship which exists between the separate terms within any set of four consecutive terms in the sequence. This relationship generates sets of Pythagorean numbers. Let the terms in the set of consecutive terms be a, b, c and d respectively; and let the first of these (a) be the nth term of the parent sequence. Then

$$(ad)^2 + (2bc)^2 = (U_{2n+3})^2$$

If a, b, c and d are 2, 3, 5 and 8 respectively; then $n = 3$, since a is the third term in the parent sequence. Then

$$U_{2n+3} = U_9$$

that is, the ninth term of the parent sequence, and this term is 34. Accordingly

$$(2.8)^2 + (2.3.5)^2 = 34^2$$
or
$$16^2 + \quad 30^2 = 34^2$$

There is also a connection between the terms of the Fibonacci sequence and the coefficients of the expansion of the binomial $(x + 1)^n$ for positive integral values of n. These coefficients may be built up as in Pascal's triangle. (See Fig. 20)

When $n = 4, (x + 1)^n = (x + 1)^4 = x^4 + 4x^3 + 6x^2 + 4x + 1$ and the coefficients can be read off direct from the row in the triangle relative to the given value of n.

If we now sum the terms in the diagonals indicated by the dots in the triangle, these respective sums will again produce, in their correct order, the terms of the Fibonacci sequence.

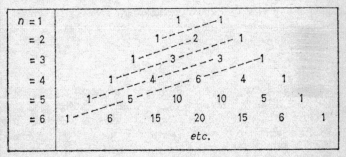

Fig. 20

There are two surprising relationships involving the squares of the terms in the Fibonacci sequence. The sum of the squares of the first n terms in the sequence is equal to the product of the nth and $(n + 1)$th term. The sum of the squares of the first five terms is

$$1 + 1 + 4 + 9 + 25 = 40$$

The fifth and sixth terms of the sequence are 5 and 8 respectively and their product is also 40.

The results of summing the squares of consecutive pairs of terms are even more satisfying. These take us full cycle back to the original sequence! The squares of the first six terms of the sequence are

$$1 \quad 1 \quad 4 \quad 9 \quad 25 \quad 64$$

Adding consecutive pairs will produce the sums

$$2 \quad 5 \quad 13 \quad 34 \quad 89$$

which are the odd terms in the original sequence; and the differences between the consecutive terms of this sequence of sums are

$$3 \quad 8 \quad 21 \quad 55$$

and these are the even terms of the original sequence.

The cubes of any three consecutive terms of the Fibonacci
sequence are related so that the sum of the cubes of the two
greater terms less the cube of the least term always gives a result
which is also a term in the parent sequence. The cubes of 2, 3 and
5, for example, give the result:

$$3^3 + 5^3 - 2^3 = 144$$

and 144 is also a term of the Fibonacci sequence; it is, incidentally, also the only term (other than 1) which is a perfect square.

Other interesting properties of the sequence include: consecutive terms are prime to each other; the greatest common
divisor of two Fibonacci numbers is itself also a Fibonacci
number; and the term U_n of the sequence is divisible by the term
U_m if n is divisible by m. But the most remarkable property of all
is that peculiar to one of the terms in the sequence. The number
89 has the astonishing property in the manner in which its
reciprocal in the scale of 10 can be represented

$$\frac{1}{89} = \cdot 0112358$$
$$13$$
$$21$$
$$34$$
$$55$$
$$89$$
$$144$$
$$233$$
$$\cdots$$
$$\overline{}$$
$$\cdot 01123595505 \cdots$$

The terms of the sequence in their correct order build up this
decimal equivalent. The addition of further decimal increments

based on the terms of the Fibonacci sequence will give the value of $1 \div 89$ to yet more significant figures.

The establishment of many of the relationships within the Fibonacci sequence depends upon the possibility of proving a formula for the nth term, for any value of n. This is by no means so simple as the above results may suggest, and the proof itself is too long to reproduce here. The formula for the nth term has a daunting look:

$$U_n = \frac{\left(\dfrac{1 + \sqrt{5}}{2}\right)^n - \left(\dfrac{1 - \sqrt{5}}{2}\right)^n}{\sqrt{5}} \qquad \ldots\ldots\text{(i)}.$$

This is called the Binet formula after the mathematician who derived it.

Perhaps the oddest thing about this is that whereas the sequence is of integers, we have the intrusion of irrational roots into the formula. Fortunately for ease in calculating, these roots cancel out directly although the calculations become progressively more difficult as the value of n increases. When $n = 2$, the numerator in the formula simplifies to $\sqrt{5}$; so that

$$U_2 = \sqrt{5} \div \sqrt{5} = 1$$

It is at first surprising to reflect that the same result is obtained when $n = 1$; although this may be rapidly confirmed from the formula.

An ingenious method exists for calculating the value of the nth term, for any specific value of n, where the full working required by the above formula would be too protracted. This method is derived from the formula and is based on the theorem that the nth term in the sequence is equal to the integer which is nearest to the nth term of the geometric progression whose first term and whose common ratio are, respectively:

$$\text{1st term: } \frac{1}{\sqrt{5}}\left(\frac{1 + \sqrt{5}}{2}\right) \quad \text{Ratio: } \frac{1 + \sqrt{5}}{2}$$

This theorem might not seem to simplify matters, but the use of logarithms alters the position materially.

To find the 12th term in the sequence, we calculate this as being equal to the nearest integer to:

$$\frac{1}{\sqrt{5}}\left(\frac{1+\sqrt{5}}{2}\right)^{12} \text{ or } \frac{(1\cdot618034)^{12}}{\sqrt{5}} \text{ approx.}$$

$$\log 1\cdot618034 = 0\cdot20898$$

$$\therefore 12 \log 1\cdot618034 = 2\cdot50776$$
$$\log \sqrt{5} \quad = 0\cdot34949$$

$$\text{subtract} \quad 2\cdot15827$$

$2\cdot15827$ is the logarithm of $144\cdot001$; so the 12th term in the sequence is the integer nearest to this value, which is 144.

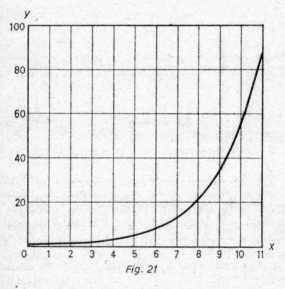

Fig. 21

Both the origin and the implication of this method are well worth inspection. The nth term of the sequence is equal to the integer nearest to a value, which we shall call y, where $y = (1\cdot618034)^n \div \sqrt{5}$. If we replace n by x, where x is a variable which may have any value (that is, it is not restricted to integral values), then we may regard the successive values of n as specific integral values of x. This being so, we may express the general function as

$$y = (1 \cdot 618034)^x \div \sqrt{5}$$

This function may be represented by a continuous curve as in Fig. 21. It should be mentioned here that the value $(1 + \sqrt{5}) \div 2 = 1 \cdot 618034$ is only an approximate value. It is, of course, an irrational. We shall continue to use this value throughout.

This is an exponential function (that is, the variable x appears as the exponent or power) the successive values of which represent a type of continuous growth.

The values of y, relative to some of the integral (n) values of x, are:

$x = n$	y	Fibonacci term
1	0·7236	1
2	1·1708	1
3	1·8944	2
4	3·0652	3
5	4·9597	5
6	8·0249	8
7	12·9846	13

It will be seen that the terms in the sequence so closely approximate to the y values that, after the first three terms, they lie almost exactly on the curve. This is a remarkable and unusual relationship between a set of continuous quantities (the values derived from the exponential function), which can take any value, and a set of discrete quantities (derived from the sequence) which can take only values which differ among themselves by certain fixed amounts.

This is of great interest in itself and tends to overshadow certain other connections which it has been suggested the Fibonacci sequence has with nature, quite apart from fictitious rabbit dynasties. These tend to be restricted mainly to botanical specimens. There are, for instance, many kinds of plants which normally have 3, 5, or 8 petals – all these numbers being contained in the sequence. Other numbers in the sequence also appear in other plants. There are, however, few plants with 2 petals, although 2 is in the sequence, whereas there are many plants with 4 petals, and 4 is not in the sequence. There is possibly no special reason for attaching significance to the appearance of particular kinds of numbers in this connection.

Of more interest, perhaps, are the arrays of florets in the heads of some kinds of flowers. In the daisy, for example, the florets in a typical specimen appear to be arrayed in two families of spiral curves – 13 florets in one direction (e.g. a right-handed spiral) and 21 florets in the other direction (e.g. a left-handed spiral). Similarly, spirals on sunflower discs may have 34 and 55 or greater numbers of florets, these numbers again being equal to terms of the Fibonacci sequence. There is no apparent reason why this should be so. We can only note the coincidence, if such it be, and move on.

We are on safer ground in trying to discover the reason for the appearance of the irrational root in the Binet formula mentioned above. This reason is by no means an obvious one and yet it is nevertheless a very simple one. It results from the solution of a quadratic equation and arises in such a way as to connect the Fibonacci sequence with the geometrical ideal of the golden section or divine proportion which was so beloved of the Greeks.

Ratios between consecutive terms of the sequence approach successively more closely to the number 1·618034... Thus:

| Consecutive terms | | Ratio $\frac{a}{b}$ |
a	b	
1	1	1·0
2	1	2·0
3	2	1·5
5	3	1·66
...	...	....
233	144	1·618055
377	233	1·618025
610	377	1·618037
987	610	1·618033
...	...	etc.

The ratios are alternately less than and greater than 1·618034. This is the equivalent of $(1 + \sqrt{5})/2$ and is the common ratio between the terms of the geometric progression used above in the special method of calculating the value of the nth term in the Fibonacci sequence. The fact that successive ratios between consecutive terms of the sequence do approach this value also show why the special method is valid. This ratio, however, also arises quite naturally out of a geometrical proposition.

Golden section in geometry refers to the division of a line segment into two parts so that the greater part is the mean proportional between the smaller part and the whole segment; that is, the whole segment is to the greater part as the greater part is to the smaller part.

It is not altogether clear why the Greeks regarded this combination of proportions to have especial merit, although they seem to have found as much significance in this as they did in the concept of number. It is true that when applied to art and architecture it does seem to have had a particular aesthetic appeal for them.

Those who have studied the work of the great artist Phidias assure us that the properties of the golden section may be seen in his sculptures. Thus, of a typical statue of 34 units height, other relative measurements might be: feet to navel, 21 units; navel to crown of head, 13 units; crown to breastline, 8 units; breastline to navel 5 units. This would seem to show an early concern for vital statistics and was possibly an attempt to anticipate modern statistical concepts by casting into stone the conglomerative attributes of the average man!

Although 'golden' figures do seem to be well proportioned it is nevertheless true that some other figures with quite different proportions are also aesthetically satisfying. Perhaps as much, or as little, significance should be attached to golden section, as being anything more than an arbitrary level of aesthetics in art, as may be attributed to the natural Fibonacci-type occurrences referred to earlier.

Golden section does, however, have an intriguing mathematical aesthetic content. The derivation of its appropriate formula may most easily be visualized from the division of a line segment into two parts so that the smaller part is of 1 unit length. Let the greater part be A units long, so that the total length of the segment is $(A + 1)$ units; to be in golden section these lengths must satisfy the proportion:

$$\frac{A + 1}{A} = \frac{A}{1}$$

whence $A^2 - A - 1 = 0$; the positive root of which equation is

$$A = \frac{1 + \sqrt{5}}{2} = 1 \cdot 618034$$

(the negative root may be ignored since we have taken the value of A as positive in the nature of our construction).

The above value represents the proportion of the greater quantity to the lesser quantity; the reciprocal proportion – that is, the proportion of the lesser quantity to the greater quantity – is sometimes quoted. That is

$$\frac{A}{A + 1} = \frac{1}{A}$$

Since $A = 1 \cdot 618034$, then its reciprocal $= 0 \cdot 618034$ (see equation (ii) below) and the ratio is therefore

$$\frac{1}{A} = 0 \cdot 618034 = (-1 + \sqrt{5}) \div 2$$

It may be noted in passing that the reciprocal of $(1 + \sqrt{5})/2$ is $(-1 + \sqrt{5})/2$, a result which would not have been intuitively anticipated.

These results lead to the following relationships:

$(1 \cdot 618034)^2 - 1$	$= 1 \cdot 618034$	(i)
$(1 \cdot 618034)(0 \cdot 61834)$	$= 1$	(ii)
$(0 \cdot 618034) \div (1 - 0 \cdot 618034)$	$= 1 \cdot 618034$	(iii)
$(2 \cdot 618034)(1 - 0 \cdot 618034)$	$= 1$	(iv)
$(2 \cdot 618034)(0 \cdot 618034)$	$= 1 \cdot 618034$	(v)

These multiple results appear to exhibit something of the miraculous although they are, in fact, all implicit in the one main result obtained above.

A further interesting connection between golden section and the Fibonacci sequence is revealed in the discovery that the ratio $(1 + \sqrt{5}) \div 2$, which occurs in the former, may be represented by the continued fraction

$$1 + \cfrac{1}{1 + \cfrac{1}{1 + \cfrac{1}{1 + \dots}}}$$

and that the convergents (i.e. successive values) of this fraction are equal to the ratios of the consecutive terms of the sequence:

$$\frac{1}{1} \quad \frac{2}{1} \quad \frac{3}{2} \quad \frac{5}{3} \quad \frac{8}{5} \text{ and so on}$$

The property of golden section occurs in many geometrical propositions. For example, if the side (a) of a regular decagon (a polygon with ten equal sides) inscribed within a circle of radius (r) is laid off along that radius, the latter will be divided in golden section.

The length of any side of a regular polygon can be expressed in trigonometrical terms relative to the angle subtended at the centre (of the inscribed circle) by the side. For a polygon having n sides, this angle is $360° \div 2n$; so that for a decagon the subtended angle is $18°$. It can then be shown that the length of the side is equal to $2r \sin 18°$.

The ratio of the radius to the side will therefore be

$$\frac{r}{2r \sin 18°} = \frac{1}{2 \sin 18°}$$

From tables we obtain the value $\sin 18° = 0 \cdot 309017$; whence $2 \sin 18° = 0 \cdot 618034$, the reciprocal of which is $1 \cdot 618034$ as has been previously noted.

This example is of particular interest in that it relates golden section to a specific trigonometrical ratio. As soon as it is possible to do this, it is usually also possible to introduce other trigonometrical ratios into associated propositions because of the relationships which exist between these ratios themselves. It has been seen that $2 \sin 18° = 0.618034$; now also it can be noted from our tables that $2 \cos 36° = 1.618034$. This equivalent is useful in a further example in which golden section almost excels itself.

In Fig. 22, FGHJK is a regular pentagon. If we produce the sides of this figure we can form a star-shaped figure, called a pentagram, whose vertices are at A, B, C, D and E. These vertices

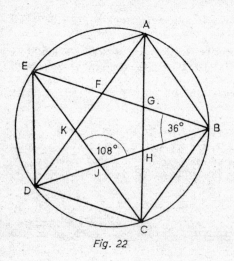

Fig. 22

all lie on one and the same circle and also coincide with the vertices of another pentagon inscribed within that circle. The star construction may thus be regarded as consisting of the diagonals of this larger pentagon.

These properties display a symmetry of great aesthetic appeal, but there are also further hidden qualities which make the pentagram a very remarkable figure indeed. A minor but nevertheless interesting property lies in the simplicity with which it may be drawn. The pentagram and, indeed, the whole of Fig. 22 is unicursal; it can be drawn in one continuous process without lifting the pencil from the paper and without traversing any part of it more than once.

A much more esoteric attribute of the pentagram relates to its golden section properties. In triangle EBJ we have angle EJB = 108°; angle EBJ = 36°. Then by the sine law, which holds that the sides of a triangle are proportional to the sines of the opposite angles,

$$\frac{EB}{EJ} = \frac{\sin 108°}{\sin 36} = \frac{\sin 72°}{\text{sn } 36}$$

(This follows from the identity $\sin \theta = \sin (180° - \theta)$; so $\sin 108° = \sin (180° - 108°) = \sin 72°$).

The values of $\sin 72°$ and $\sin 36°$ may be read off from printed tables and the above ratio will be found to be equal to 1·618034. But it can also be shown, by a transformation of the trigonometrical equivalent $\sin 2A = 2 \sin A . \cos A$, that $\sin 72° \div \sin 36° = 2 \cos 36°$ so that the value of the above ratio may more easily be calculated by doubling the value of $\cos 36°$.

The lines EB and EJ are thus seen to be in golden section relationship. But EJ = EG; so EB and EG also have the same ratio. In fact, the diagonal EB is divided off in such a way that each of the segments FG, EF, EG and EB is 1·618034 times as great as the next preceding segment in the order shown. Furthermore each of the other diagonals is divided in exactly the same way and is also 1·618034 times as great as each of the sides, such as EA, of the larger inscribed pentagon.

And as if the properties of the pentagram (or pentacle, as it was sometimes called) were not sufficient in themselves, the figure was for long regarded as having mysterious powers quite beyond anything which could be ascribed to its geometric qualities. The Pythagoreans adopted it as the sacred and mystic symbol of their brotherhood. In the Middle Ages it was much favoured by necromancers and it was also widely used as a charm to ward off the undesirable attention of witches and evil spirits. Faust duly banished Mephistopheles with its aid but, alas for the elusive triumph over evil, little good it seems to have done him in the long run.

Golden section occurs also in relationships between the metrical properties of regular solid figures which have plane faces and straight edges. An icosahedron (having 20 triangular faces) can be inscribed within an octohedron (having 8 triangular faces) of appropriate dimensions, so that each vertex of the former divides one of the edges of the latter in golden section. This proposition involves a delicate intricacy which is surprising enough in itself; but like so many of the rewards of mathematics it is also remarkable that anyone could even have ever contemplated such a possibility, let alone to have demonstrated it successfully.

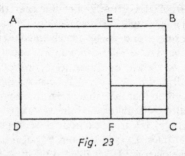

Fig. 23

Rectangles which have their respective sides in a golden section relationship have a built-in property which gives rise to an infinite process of 'exhaustion'. In Fig. 23 ABCD is a rectangle whose sides AD and AB are 2 and $(1 + \sqrt{5})$ units respectively. That is:

$$AB \div AD = (1 + \sqrt{5}) \div 2 = 1 \cdot 618034.$$

The sides of the rectangle are thus in golden section, and the rectangle may therefore be called a golden rectangle.

The line EF is drawn so as to form the square AEFD with a side of 2 units. Then AE = 2; and EB = $(1 + \sqrt{5}) - 2 = (-1 + \sqrt{5})$. Consequently in the rectangle EBCF

$$\frac{EF}{EB} = \frac{2}{-1 + \sqrt{5}} = \frac{1 + \sqrt{5}}{2} = 1 \cdot 618034$$

So that this is also a golden rectangle. Again, if we draw the largest square possible within this rectangle (the square being of side $(-1 + \sqrt{5})$ units) then the next remaining rectangle will also be golden.

This process may in theory be continued indefinitely and the remaining rectangle at each stage will always be golden. Of course the squares and the rectangles will be smaller at each successive stage, and the area of the original rectangle may thus be 'exhausted' almost completely – in fact to as great a degree as we like to take the process.

The process is akin to that involved in calculus; the value 1·618034 is the 'limiting value' of the ratio of consecutive Fibonacci terms, and the concept of limits will also be seen, in the next chapter, to play an essential role in the calculus.

6. Vanishing Tricks and Calculus

Some fractions have a disconcerting habit of suddenly disappearing without giving any prior notice of their intention. This apparently wilful behaviour is, in fact, inherent in their structure. For example, the fraction

$$\frac{x^2 - 6x + 8}{x^2 - 5x + 4}$$

looks straightforward enough; but when $x = 4$, this reduces to $0/0$ which is as confoundedly insubstantial and provoking as the grin left behind by the Cheshire Cat.

This is an example of a vanishing fraction, although this term is perhaps not entirely satisfactory since, instead of vanishing altogether, the fraction leaves us with a conundrum. The form $0/0$ is not equal to zero. It is indeterminate and operates rather like a no-entry sign which impedes our otherwise smooth progress and prevents us from making a direct approach to our objective.

If we divide both the numerator and the denominator of the above fraction by their common factor $(x - 4)$, the fraction simplifies to

$$\frac{x - 2}{x - 1}$$

When $x = 4$, this simplified fraction is equal to $2/3$. What then really is the true value of the original fraction?

The fraction proves to be indeterminate when $x = 4$, because it is of the form

$$\frac{(x - 2)\,(x - 4)}{(x - 1)\,(x - 4)}$$

and, of course, when $x = 4$, the common factor $(x - 4) = 0$. Thus, although it is normally legitimate to cancel out common factors we are, when $x = 4$, in effect purporting to divide the numerator and the denominator by zero, a process much frowned upon.

This predicament occurs only when $x = 4$. It does not occur, for example, when $x = 3.999$ or 4.001, so that we may obtain a determinate solution for any value of x as near to $x = 4$ as we like. If $x = 4.001$ then $(x - 4)$ is not zero and we can cancel out this common factor with an easy conscience; and we can also calculate the exact value of the fraction relative to this value of x.

Nevertheless this does not give a value directly associated with the value $x = 4$, and we need to try a different approach. So instead of calculating the value of the fraction for the value $x = 4.001$, we may calculate the value of the fraction when $x = (4 + h)$, where h is indefinitely small.

When $x = (4 + h)$ we may again cancel out the common factor $(x - 4)$ since this will be equal to h which, although indefinitely small, is not zero. The fraction

$$\frac{x - 2}{x - 1} \text{ becomes } \frac{2 + h}{3 + h}$$

Then as we take values of x closer and closer to 4, so h will take values closer and closer to zero, and the value of the fraction will move closer and closer to 2/3. Whatever value of h we may select, there will always be a smaller value we could have selected instead without h ever being taken as zero. To take $h = 0$ would merely restore the conundrum. The value of h can by an infinite process be made to approach zero and the value which it thus approaches is called its limiting value or limit. Similarly as h approaches zero, so $(2 + h) \div (3 + h)$ approaches 2/3 as its limit.

The concept of limit is essential to the rigorous formulation of calculus theory since it overcomes certain logical difficulties which otherwise tend to arise in considering the properties of infinite processes. In general, if y is a function of x, expressed as $y = f(x)$, and if, when x approaches a value a, the function can be made to differ by as little as we please from a fixed quantity b, then b is called the limit of y when $x = a$.

A common example of an infinite process and its associated limit is provided by the sequence

$$1 \quad \tfrac{1}{2} \quad \tfrac{1}{4} \quad \tfrac{1}{8} \quad \cdots$$

This sequence has successive terms each of which, after the first, is exactly one half of the next preceding term. The numbers in the sequence are successively smaller; they approach zero but never reach it. The sequence is infinite and there is no 'last' number. One half of any positive number must always be greater than zero.

That is: (a) given any term greater than zero, we can always find another term closer to but still greater than zero, and (b) no finite number of terms will produce a value which is exactly equal to or less than zero. Consequently, the limit of the sequence must be zero.

If we now sum the terms of this sequence to produce the series

$$1 + \tfrac{1}{2} + \tfrac{1}{4} + \tfrac{1}{8} + \cdots$$

we shall obtain a total or rather a series of totals which approach the value 2 as we take more and more terms into the sum. Thus as the terms of the sequence approach zero, so the sum of the series formed by those terms approaches the limit 2. Here is a vital clue to the usefulness of the limit concept. If we know the limiting value of one infinite process, it is often possible to deduce from this the limiting value of an associated process.

The application of the limit concept to geometry may be demonstrated by a method used by Archimedes to calculate the approximate value of π, although the limit concept in fact enables us to proceed, in wider applications, beyond the field of mere approximations.

If a regular polygon (all the sides of which are equal each to each) is inscribed within a circle, then the area of the polygon will clearly be less than that of the circle. On the other hand, the area of a polygon circumscribed about a circle will be greater than the area of the circle. But as the number of sides of the polygons is increased, so the sides themselves will become shorter and the areas of the two polygons will approximate more closely to the area of the circle. The area of the inscribed polygon will give an approximation which is less than the area of the circle; the circumscribed polygon will provide an approximation which is greater.

The inscribed and circumscribed polygons thus trap the circle between them. Their perimeters approach identity with the circumference of the circle and the latter provides a limiting form beyond which they cannot progress. This is an infinite process and the length of the circumference may therefore be regarded as the limiting length of the perimeters of regular polygons as their sides are made smaller and smaller – that is, as the latter approach zero length.

As a trap for the circumference of a circle, Archimedes used polygons having ninety-six sides and, by calculating the ratio between the diagonal and perimeter within each polygon, he was able to show that the value of π was less than $3\frac{1}{7}$ but greater than $3\frac{10}{71}$.

The very idea of a polygon with sides so small that it might eventually become a circle, or of a polygon with an infinite number of infinitely small sides was so preposterous and self-contradictory that the Greeks would never have entertained the mere possibility with any seriousness. The philospher Antiphon did indeed suggest some such identity between polygons and circles, but his ideas were so advanced, heretical even, for the mathematics of his time. It was an intriguing mental exercise; no doubt the Greeks had a word for it, but whatever that word was, it was not mathematics.

Yet Antiphon had perhaps seen a glimmer of the truth. It is still not claimed that a polygon would ever become a circle, or that an infinite sequence would ever reach its limiting value; it might indeed be said that the usefulness of limiting values would disappear if they could. Fortunately, this question does not really arise.

In using limits we approach the measurement of quantities indirectly because we cannot successfully measure them directly. Despite the indirectness of approach the results, properly obtained, are nevertheless exact. With consummate ease we may pluck a finite result from an infinite process; there is, of course, no more of the occult in this than there is in the legerdemain of the accomplished conjuror, but it is equally intriguing to observe.

We cannot by ordinary finite methods calculate the exact sum of the series $1 + \frac{1}{2} + \frac{1}{4} + \frac{1}{8} \ldots$ since the additive process is also finite. Yet we have seen above that the limiting value of this sum is 2 – no more and no less. The limit is a finite quantity which the infinite process approaches.

If, then, it is the limit itself in which we are interested, we may happily proceed with our calculations in the sure knowledge that it is a finite quantity. The fact that this limit is associated with an infinite process, and doubts as to whether such a process can ever reach its limit are as entirely irrelevant as is the inability of the exhausted and lonely long-distance runner to complete his race if we are interested only in the position of the finishing line. The tape is there whether he finishes or not and it is the tape, not the runner, which is our prime concern.

The calculus, as originally developed, was based upon methods other than those involving limiting values. That these methods could be used and that, so far as could be seen, they apparently gave correct results was widely accepted; but it was not possible to demonstrate with mathematical rigour that the results were necessarily correct.

Furthermore, the principles involved appeared to encourage a number of frustrating paradoxes and contradictions and this not unnaturally caused some lively comment from quite unexpected quarters. The validity of the principles could not be proved and there was accordingly some suspicion of guilt about their dubious parentage. These paradoxes will be noted at the end of the chapter. The results obtained from the propositions of calculus, however, were so remarkable as to be a prime source of wonderment. Today these same propositions may be proved with mathematical rigour, but the wonder at the achievements of calculus is still as fresh and as lively as ever.

Calculus is one of the greatest applied tools which mathematics has ever fashioned. It enters into calculations in almost every science and has, indeed, assisted in the actual development of science. It is of immense importance in nuclear physics and space travel and it has contributed largely to the astonishing technological progress of the last few decades. It has proved of vital importance both in peace and in war; and it is appropriate that W. S. Gilbert's model of a modern major-general should be able to claim that he was very good at integral and differential calculus – even though Gilbert was in fact implying that it wasn't.

The applications of calculus are many and diverse. These are of interest themselves, but they normally have their greatest impact in highly sophisticated scientific structures which do not lend themselves to explanation in simple terms. Fortunately there is a greater fascination to be derived from the intriguing characteristics of calculus itself. It is certainly full of surprises.

The principles of differential calculus and those of integral calculus derive from apparently different considerations although they each employ the same basic mathematical concept of limit, and it is no less than astonishing to discover eventually that the one may be regarded as the inverse of the other. This is one of the supreme examples of the dove-tailing propensities of mathematics.

The most difficult transition in mathematics is from the discrete to the continuous, from the straight line to the curve, and from statics to dynamics. These posed very real problems for the earlier mathematicians and caused intense frustration and perplexity. Yet calculus enables us to bridge the chasm in a mighty stride.

Differential calculus deals mainly with problems involving rates of change in the values of variable quantities such as speed (rate of change of distance relative to time) or acceleration (rate of change of speed) or, in general, the rate of change in a variable relative to another.

The function $y = x^2$ implies that there is a unique corresponding value of y for each separate value of x. As x varies, so does y vary, although not at the same rate. If y represents distance (in feet) travelled and x represents time (in seconds) [then, for any specified number of seconds], we may at once calculate the relative distance traversed. When $x = 4$; so $y = 16$; so that in four seconds sixteen feet will be travelled.

From the same data we may calculate the average speed during any given number of seconds. Sixteen feet are travelled in four seconds, and the average speed during that period is therefore 4 ft per sec. But in ten seconds, the distance travelled is one hundred feet (that is $x = 10$; $y = 100$); so that the average speed during this period is 10 ft per sec. The speed is actually increasing and will continue to increase within the limitations implicit in the physical conditions which the function describes. How then is it possible to calculate the speed at any particular instant?

Algebraic methods can give us average speeds during any given periods of time but it is often necessary to calculate a speed (of a vehicle, for example) at a specific point of time. Algebra alone cannot supply the answer.

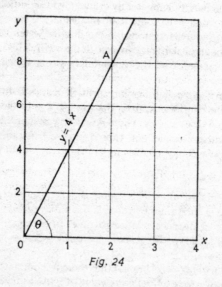

Fig. 24

Distance and time variables are both continuous and between any two arbitrarily chosen values they take on all possible values in a truly literal sense. These include fractional values. This is where the difficulty arises because there is an infinitude of fractions between any two consecutive whole numbers and, what is more confusing, there is also an infinitude of fractions between any two fractions we care to specify no matter how small the latter may be. As the fractions are made smaller so the actual difference between them becomes smaller, but there are still more fractions which can be found. This process may be continued indefinitely and, since the speed is increasing continuously, it will be different for each and every instant of time.

It may seem presumptuous to suppose that we can establish an extremely simple formula which will enable us to trap this notion of speed at any instant, or instantaneous speed, when it is never the same from one instant to another. The fact is, however, that we can do just this. Before attempting this, it will be helpful to fix some basic ideas in a study of uniform speed.

The function $y = 4x$ is represented by the curve in Fig. 24 (y is distance in feet; x is time in seconds).

A is any point on the curve. AB is parallel to the y axis. It will first be apparent that the slope of this curve relative to the axes will depend upon the nature of the function represented. The curve of the function $y = 3x$ would be less steep; the curve of the function $y = 5x$ would be steeper still. The gradient of the curve is measured by the trigonometrical ratio derived from the triangle ABO.

$$\frac{\text{height}}{\text{base}} = \frac{AB}{OB} = \tan \theta$$

But AB, the ordinate at A, represents distance; and OB, the abscissa, represents time. Consequently, the ratio $AB \div OB$ also expresses average speed over the relevant time interval.

$$\frac{AB}{OB} = \text{gradient} = \tan \theta = \frac{8}{2} = 4$$

thus giving an average speed of 4 ft per sec.

If we draw other ordinates at any other points on the curve, the triangles thus formed will all be similar to triangle ABO. Each triangle will contain the angle θ, that is angle AOB, and in each instance, therefore, $\tan \theta = 4$. This is because the curve is in fact a straight line and the angle θ is constant. The average speed throughout is uniform at 4 ft per sec.

This result may be approached in a more formalized manner.
A is any point on the curve representing a related pair of values
of x and y. As x grows, so does y grow. Let x grow very slightly
by the addition of an increment represented by the symbol $\triangle x$,
so that x becomes $(x + \triangle x)$ at point D on the curve. Let the
resultant increment in y (as a result of the growth in x) be $\triangle y$;
then y will become $(y + \triangle y)$ at point D.

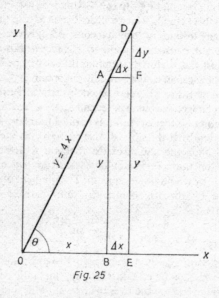

Fig. 25

In Fig. 25, AF is drawn parallel to BE and by construction
these two segments are equal in length and represent $\triangle x$. DF
represents $\triangle y$. The triangle DFA is similar to triangle ABO.
Therefore

$$\frac{DF}{AF} = \frac{\triangle y}{\triangle x} = \tan \theta$$

and this is true no matter what value of x we first select and no
matter what size we make $\triangle x$.

By the functional relationship the value of y is always four times
as great as the value of x. Consequently, the new value of y, that

is $(y + \triangle y)$ will be four times as great as the new value of x, that is $(x + \triangle x)$. So

$$y + \triangle y = 4(x + \triangle x)$$
$$= 4x + 4\triangle x$$

but $$y = 4x$$

Subtracting: $$\triangle y = \qquad 4\triangle x$$

Whence $$\frac{\triangle y}{\triangle x} = 4$$

Again we obtain the result: average speed is 4 ft per sec.

This is calculated as the average speed but we can choose a value of $\triangle x$ as small as we like – so small indeed that it may be indistinguishable from a single point – and this average speed will always be the same. The speed is, in fact, uniform throughout.

We now apply similar methods in respect of a function whose rate of increase is not uniform. Fig. 26 shows the curve of $y = 16x^2$.

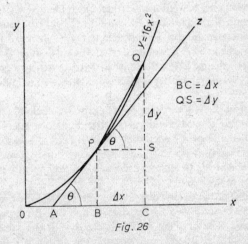

Fig. 26

P is any point on the curve. What is the rate of change at this point precisely? For a straight line curve we can measure this rate of change at *any* point by the gradient of the curve as a whole. Our present curve, however, is not straight and we cannot take the same easy course. The problem, then, must be converted to measuring the gradient of the curve at point P.

This is much simpler than might be imagined, and it may be shown* that the gradient of a curve at any point is the same as the gradient of the tangent to the curve at the same point. This proposition may be demonstrated by employing an apparent paradox which, like the paradoxes of G. K. Chesterton, proves to have a highly enlightening value. Although the rate of change of the function is increasing continuously, the simplest way of solving our problem is to suppose that it isn't or, more specifically, that it suddenly stops increasing at P.

Suppose that the rate of change increases right up to the value of x represented by point P but that it then remains uniform at the rate already achieved at that point; then from P onwards the curve would be a straight line in the direction of Z. The line PZ will then also be the tangent to the curve at P since no other point can be on both the original curve and PZ. Thus PZ touches the curve at only one point and is therefore the tangent at that point.

The rate of change along PZ is uniform, being the same as at P by hypothesis, and this is equivalent to $\tan \theta$, where θ is the angle made by the line PZ if produced to cut the x axis at A. Conversely the rate of change at P is the same as that everywhere along PZ; if we can measure the latter we shall also at the same time measure the former.

The problem is thus changed yet again to calculating the value of $\tan \theta$. We cannot rely upon construction alone since, in order to be able to draw AZ accurately, we first need to know the value of θ. We cannot do this the other way round. However, the measurement of $\tan \theta$ may be achieved quite simply by using the limit concept.

P and Q are separate points on the curve. QC is the ordinate at Q. P and Q are joined by the straight line PQ. PS is parallel to the x axis. The gradient of PQ is clearly not the same as the gradient of AZ. By moving Q nearer and nearer to P, however, the line PQ would become shorter and the angle SPQ would approach equality with the angle SPZ, since the line PQ would also move in a clockwise direction towards line AZ.

*See footnote page 99.

This is our infinite process. As the length of **PQ** approaches zero, so the angle **SPQ** approaches θ. That is, the limiting value of the angle **SPQ** is θ. In the triangle **QSP**, then

$$\tan SPQ = \frac{QS}{SP} = \frac{\triangle y}{\triangle x}$$

Since θ is the limiting value of the angle **SPQ**, then $\tan \theta$ is the limiting value of $\tan SPQ$ and therefore also the limiting value of the ratio $\triangle y \div \triangle x$. This limiting value is usually written as dy/dx to distinguish it and is called the derivative or differential coefficient of y with respect to x for the given function.

Our problem is accordingly transformed once more. We now need to calculate the value dy/dx and we shall at last have calculated the rate of change at **P**. An adapted form of the method previously shown for the straight-line function, coupled with the use of limits, takes us without much more ado to the solution.

For the function $y = 16x^2$ we proceed as follows:

$$y + \triangle y = 16 (x + \triangle x)^2$$
$$= 16 [x^2 + 2x\triangle x + (\triangle x)^2]$$
but
$$y = 16x^2$$
so
$$\triangle y = 16 [2x\triangle x + (\triangle x)^2]$$
$$= 32x\triangle x + 16 (\triangle x)^2$$
and
$$\frac{\triangle y}{\triangle x} = 32x + 16 \triangle x$$

$\triangle x$ may be any size we like; we may make it approach zero and, as this happens, so $32x + 16 \triangle x$ will approach $32x$. Thus the limiting value, that is the derivative

$$\frac{dy}{dx} = 32x$$

The function $y = 16x^2$ will be more familiar in the form $d = 16t^2$ where d is distance (in feet) and t is time (in seconds). This states the law of free falling bodies said to have been deduced by Galileo from the simple experiment of dropping stones from different levels of the leaning tower of Pisa, possibly to the peril of the local clergy but certainly to his own immense satisfaction. Our calculation has shown that the speed of a free falling stone (at any instant x) is $32x$ ft per sec.

It will be useful to summarize the method. We started with the function $y = 16x^2$; enlarged this to $(y + \triangle y) = 16 (x + \triangle x)^2$; expanded the binomial $(x + \triangle x)^2$; simplified the resultant expression; derived an equivalent expression for $\triangle y$; divided throughout by $\triangle x$; and finally took the limiting value of $\triangle y / \triangle x$. In the original function, the coefficient of x^2 is 16 and the exponent of x is 2. It takes little observation to note that the product of these two numbers is the same as the coefficient 32 in the derivative.

Observation does not, of course, prove anything. Nevertheless it may be shown* that the result is not a coincidence. For a simple function of the form $y = ax^n$, the derivative is always equivalent to anx^{n-1} (for non-zero values of n). This may be called a differentiation formula; differentiation being the process of identifying the derivative of a function.

How remarkably simple this solution is after all. Who, unless forewarned, could honestly have expected such an elegant outcome of so seemingly slippery a problem of trapping specific values of a variable which is changing value every instant?

We have seen that the derivative of the function $y = 16x^2$ is $32x$. This derivative is itself a function of x and varies as x varies. It may accordingly be differentiated to show the rate of change of the derivative with respect to x. The derivative of a derivative is called the second derivative of the original function and is expressed by the symbol

$$\frac{d^2y}{dx^2}$$

the numeral 2 being merely an indication that the expression is a second derivative and having no other significance whatever.

Using the differentiation formula noted above, the derivative of $y = 32x$ is

$$anx^{n-1} = 32.1.x^\circ = 32$$

since $n = 1$ and $x^\circ = 1$. So the second derivative of the function $y = 16x^2$ is also 32; this no longer depends upon the value of x and is constant for all values of x.

The first derivative of this original function, when applied to the properties of a falling stone, measures the instantaneous speed

*See footnote page 99.

of the stone. The second derivative measures the rate of change of this speed and therefore measures the acceleration of the stone. The calculus thus demonstrates the recognizable law that, given the premise that the function $y = 16x^2$ is relevant to the physical circumstances of the falling stone, then the acceleration of the latter is constant at 32 ft per sec/sec.

Integral calculus was originally conceived in connection with the measurement of shapes, but it has many applications which are not directly related to such measurements at all. Thus while it provides a method for calculating the areas and volumes of curved figures and solids it also more importantly enables us to

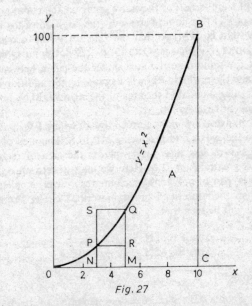

Fig. 27

measure 'the area under a curve'. This area will represent a variable which is intimately related to the function represented by the curve and the ability to measure this area will tell us something about that variable.

The curve of the function $y = x^2$ is shown in Fig. 27. If y

represents speed in feet per second and x represents time in seconds, then the area of the shape OBC (which lies between the x axis, the y ordinate at B and the arc of the curve OB) represents the total distance (in feet) travelled relative to the time values of x at O and C. The area of this shape is described as the 'area under the curve' between the values of x at O and C.

The basic idea in integral calculus is the summation of a number of values and then taking the limiting value of their sum as the number of values is indefinitely increased, the values themselves being indefinitely decreased.

The area of OBC may be split up into a number of strips of area like PQMN. Only this one strip is shown in the diagram for the sake of simplicity. Let P be any point on the curve and let the value of x at this point increase by the addition of the increment $\triangle x$ (that is, NM) so that the value of y will increase by the addition of $\triangle y$ (that is, QR) to $y + \triangle y$ at point Q on the curve. At the same time the area under the curve between the origin O and the ordinate PN will increase by the addition of an increment of area equal to the area of the strip PQMN. Let this area increment be $\triangle A$.

Two rectangles are now formed by drawing PR and SQ parallel to the x axis and producing NP to S. The area of rectangle PRMN is less than $\triangle A$, whereas the area of rectangle SQMN is greater than $\triangle A$. Here we may discern an echo of Archimedes' pair of polygons which are respectively smaller and greater than their inscribed or circumscribed circle. From the diagram it will be seen that

$$\text{Area PRMN} = y\triangle x$$
$$\text{Area SQMN} = (y + \triangle y)\triangle x$$

and accordingly

$$y\triangle x < \triangle A < (y + \triangle y)\triangle x \qquad \ldots\ldots \text{ (i)}$$

These inequalities hold for any value of $\triangle x$. $y\triangle x$ is always less than $\triangle A$, although as we make $\triangle x$ progressively smaller by moving point Q towards P, the absolute differences between the values in (i) above will gradually reduce. The smaller we make

$\triangle x$, so also the smaller will $\triangle y$ become, and line SQ will approach PR.

When $\triangle x$ is very small the area of either of the rectangles may be taken as an approximate measurement of the area of the strip, that is $\triangle A$. We can make this approximation as close as we like by making $\triangle x$ sufficiently small. Now the whole area of shape OBC may be regarded as being composed entirely of strips like PQMN, and the sum of the areas of all the rectangles like PRMN may be made to approximate as closely as we like to the total area of OBC.

The narrower the rectangles, so the closer will be this approximation to the true area under the curve. The narrowing of the rectangles may be continued indefinitely; this is our infinite process to which the limit concept may be applied. As $\triangle x$ approaches zero, so the sum of the rectangular areas approaches the total area under the curve.

We now revert to the inequality (i) above. If we divide each term by $\triangle x$, we obtain

$$y < \frac{\triangle A}{\triangle x} < (y + \triangle y)$$

Now, as $\triangle x$ approaches zero, so also does $\triangle y$ approach zero. Accordingly $(y - \triangle y)$ approaches y, while at the same time the ratio $\triangle A \div \triangle x$ will approach its own limiting form dA/dx. This limit thus appears to be neither less nor greater than y. So it must be none other than y itself. But $y = x^2$, whence

$$\frac{dA}{dx} = x^2$$

We have thus identified the derivative of the area function in terms of x. To identify the area function itself, therefore, we must be able to recognize the function which, when differentiated, would yield the derivative we have more or less stumbled upon.

In differential calculus the essential requirement is to identify the derivative of a given function. Now, in integral calculus, we need to identify the original function, or integral, of a given derivative. To do this we merely reverse the process of differentiation where this is possible.

The derivative of ax^n is anx^{n-1}. Thus the derivative of $\frac{1}{3}x^3$ is $\frac{1}{3}.3.x^{3-1} = x^2$. The area A, under the curve of $y = x^2$, has been shown to be equal to a function of which x^2 is the derivative. Hence the area under the curve is $\frac{1}{3}x^3$.

The relationship between the function represented by the curve and the function represented by the area under that curve is a totally unexpected one. It is something of a revelation that a function, which clearly may be regarded as the integral of its own derivative, may itself also be regarded as the derivative of some other function.

Either calculus may be treated as the inverse of the other; like the chicken and the egg neither can claim any precedence of origin, although integral calculus does prove to have the much wider usefulness. For one kind of calculation we move from a function to its derivative; for other kinds of problems we pass back from the derivative to its integral, that is the original or primitive function.

Yet this is no mere shuttle service of purposeless movement. A great deal may be achieved along the way whichever direction we need to follow just as Theseus, who by the aid of Adriadne's magic thread was able to find his way through the labyrinth and back again, was in the meantime also able, by taking the bull of his dilemma by the horns, to erase the appetite of the Minotaur once and for all. It may be observed, in passing, that the rewards of calculus are more lasting than those which the unfortunate Ariadne was to enjoy.

The application of the integral method to the calculation of areas is illustrated in Fig. 28. The construction is simple although the calculations are rather less so. Here we shall merely see how the method may be applied. The diagram shows a circle centred at O which is also the origin of a system of co-ordinate axes.

The part of the circumference which lies in the right-hand upper quadrant (that is, the arc VW) is also an arc of the curve of the function $y = \sqrt{(a^2 + x^2)}$. This follows from Pythagoras' theorem. OE is the radius of the circle; as the point C moves towards W, so the radius OE rotates towards OW, and E also moves towards

W. The radius has the constant value, a; but as x increases, so y decreases.

It may be shown* that the integral of the above function is $\pi a^2 \div 4$. This represents the area under the curve which is in fact the area of the circle quadrant. The area of the whole circle is therefore four times as great. The area of the circle is accordingly πa^2.

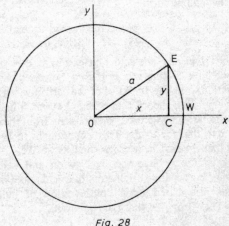

Fig. 28

It has been the purpose of this chapter to demonstrate the knitting together of the two distinctive kinds of calculus and to show some of its surprising results. It has not been the purpose to give detailed explanations of all the subject's ramifications; it might nevertheless be as well to make it clear that not all calculus is as simple as the elementary examples might suggest. There are exceptions from the basic rules of differentiation; some functions cannot as yet be integrated; and many of the more useful methods call for a high degree of ingenuity, application and care. But the basic ideas noted here are no less interesting for all that.

Finally we turn to a reconciliation between the old and the

*See *Calculus Explained*, W. J. Reichmann (Methuen London; Van Nostrand, New York).

modern views of the validity of calculus. It will be recalled that
in differentiating the function $y = 16x^2$, we first found that

$$\triangle y = 32x\triangle x + 16\,(\triangle x)^2$$

and
$$\frac{\triangle y}{\triangle x} = 32x + 16\,\triangle x$$

and then, by letting $\triangle x$ approach zero, so $\triangle y/\triangle x$ was made to
approach the limiting form

$$\frac{dy}{dx} = 32x$$

This method is logically satisfactory, at least by modern standards.

Before the limit concept was employed, however, the solution
of the equation to obtain the value of the derivative was thought
to depend upon the theory that when $\triangle x$ was infinitesimally
small it could be safely ignored when passing from the equation
for $\triangle y/\triangle x$ to that for dy/dx. This was thought to be justified
by the fact that $\triangle x$ may be made as small as we like.

The original theory favoured by Newton and Leibniz, the
contemporary but separate originators of calculus as a developed
theory, was also based upon consideration of infinitesimal
quantities. They proposed that the equation

$$\triangle y = 32x\triangle x + 16\,(\triangle x)^2$$

would become
$$dy = 32xdx + 16\,(dx)^2$$

when $\triangle x$ or dx was infinitesimally small and that, as dx itself was
infinitesimally small, any higher order of infinitesimals – for
example $(dx)^2$ – would be negligible by comparison and could
therefore be ignored. So

$$dy = 32xdx + 16\,(dx)^2$$

would become
$$dy = 32xdx$$

whence, again
$$\frac{dy}{dx} = 32x$$

Thus they arrived at the same result but the neglect of infinitesimals, while acceptable to the intuition as an obvious expedient,
could not be justified by mathematical proof, which admits

nothing as proof until it has been properly substantiated. Many problems might be 'solved' if we could ignore awkward quantities which we could not otherwise eliminate from our calculations. While ignoring such quantities may give us approximations to a solution, it is too casual a habit to validate any so-called proof.

Bishop George Berkeley was at great pains to expose this weakness of calculus and he did so with scathing wit and energy. Berkeley was not a mathematician. He was a philosopher and, although his philosophy contained some ideas which were, to say the least, insubstantive, nevertheless his comments on the calculus were very much to the point. It appears that he had been stung to rebuke the assertions of an 'infidel mathematician' (to whom his tract was addressed) that many religious doctrines were inconceivable to the reason. He retorted that the supposedly exact science of mathematics could not always justify its propositions by strict logical reasoning. He wrote:

But it should seem that this reasoning is not fair or conclusive. For when it is said, let the increments vanish (i.e. let the increments be nothing or let there be no increments) the former supposition that the increments were something, or that they were increments, is destroyed; and yet a consequence of that supposition (i.e. an expression got by virtue thereof) is retained. Certainly when we suppose the increments to vanish, we must suppose their proportions, their expressions and everything else derived from the supposition of their existence, to vanish with them . . .

Berkeley was not complaining that the results obtained by calculus were inexact; but he argued that the calculus could only lead from false premises to correct results because of the compensation of errors. He strongly objected to the mute acceptance of a maxim more suited to an illusionist's patter 'Now you see it; now you don't'. No matter how small the increments are, they are nevertheless of some size and they cannot just be disregarded. Oh the little more, as Browning observed, and how much it is!

Fortunately the use of the limit concept has overcome the difficulties and disposed of the strictures. We no longer ignore negligible infinitesimals; instead we identify a result as something which is approached and can be recognized. As in golf the approach is all-important.

None the less the calculus offers a major example of a process which was able to give results that could be accepted as correct long before anyone could prove that the conclusions really were logically valid. What a loss to mathematics if Newton (and Leibniz of course) had shrugged off calculus as invalid!

7. Among Equals

Quadratic equations may seem to offer an unpromising if not improbable source of mathematical interest. Yet they provide examples of unexpected mathematical patterns which, at a deeper level of significance, illustrate the type of inbred relationships that pose a major paradox in the philosophy of mathematics. Such patterns, which are apparently complete, fixed and self-consistent and which have about them at least a veneer of inevitability are, nevertheless, also seemingly accidental in their origin. The patterns were certainly not designed by man, although he has managed to discover some of them, and it is not conceivable that they can be the results of any positive purposeful activity of forces which lie outside mankind.

A quadratic equation is one which involves the second, but no higher, power of the unknown variable, and its general form is

$$ax^2 + bx + c = 0$$

in which the coefficients a, b, and c, are any specified quantities which are constant for a particular equation and may be either positive, negative or (except a) zero. If a is zero, the term ax^2 would disappear and the equation would reduce to the linear equation

$$bx + c = 0$$

One curious fact which emerges in the solving of quadratic equations, as also in the solving of other kinds of equations, is that although our attention is focused upon the variable x (since it is a particular value or values of this which comprise the solution of an equation) nevertheless the coefficients of the various terms in the equation are of paramount importance for our purposes. In other words, the roots of the equation (that is, the values of the variable which will satisfy the equation) can be expressed entirely in terms of the coefficients a, b, and c. Of course, if this were not so, we would be unable to solve the general equation.

Linear equations have the same sort of general property, as also have cubic and quartic (or biquadratic) equations – that is, equations involving the first, third and fourth powers of x respectively. It will be noted later, however, that this facility for the extraction of roots does not extend to equations of degree higher than the fourth.

The formula for the roots of a quadratic equation is the familiar one:

$$x = \frac{-b \pm \sqrt{(b^2 - 4ac)}}{2a}$$

which most of us will have learned at school and probably have long since forgotten. It is derived by the device of 'completing the square' as follows:

$$ax^2 + bx + c = 0$$
so
$$ax^2 + bx = -c$$
and
$$x^2 + \frac{bx}{a} = -\frac{c}{a}$$

adding the square of half the coefficient of x to each side gives

$$x^2 + \frac{bx}{a} + \left(\frac{b}{2a}\right)^2 = \left(\frac{b}{2a}\right)^2 - \frac{c}{a}$$

so
$$\left(x + \frac{b}{2a}\right)^2 = \frac{b^2 - 4ac}{4a^2}$$

from which the final equivalent for x is found by taking the square root of each side and subtracting the term $(b \div 2a)$ from both sides.

Thus we have a remarkably compact, if slightly complicated, formula with which we can solve any quadratic equation. It is an enduring tool which never blunts and is usually accepted merely as an aid to computation. But it is of much greater significance than this since it embodies the principle of generality for which mathematicians strive in all their research endeavours. It also illustrates that such generality either imposes its own restrictions or is itself possible only because of the restrictions.

The roots of a quadratic equation can always be expressed in terms of its coefficients. If we reverse our thinking, we must inevitably conclude that it is impossible to form an equation from arbitrarily selected 'roots' in such a way that the roots cannot be represented in terms of the coefficients of that equation. Quadratic equations, and some others, may accordingly be regarded as having a fixed, self-contained and closed structure of their own. Within this structure there are yet more interesting relationships and properties to be discerned.

Every quadratic equation has just two roots and no more; and these may be either real or imaginary (that is, involving the imaginary number $\sqrt{-1}$; see Chapter 10) and, if real, either rational or irrational according to certain conditions inherent in the structure of particular equations. For example, if $(b^2 - 4ac)$ is negative, then the roots will be imaginary; but otherwise they will be real, and we can ascertain, by calculating this value, whether the roots are real or imaginary without actually solving the equation. This quantity is accordingly called the discriminant of the equation. When it is zero the roots are real and equal; thus in the equation

$$x^2 - 6x + 9 = 0$$

the value of $(b^2 - 4ac)$ is $36 - 36 = 0$. Both roots of this equation are equal to 3, as may be seen from the factorization

$$(x - 3)(x - 3) = 0$$

The two roots of a quadratic equation are

$$\frac{-b + \sqrt{(b^2 - 4ac)}}{2a} \text{ and } \frac{-b - \sqrt{(b^2 - 4ac)}}{2a}$$

The sum of these two roots may be seen by inspection to reduce to the simple form $-b/a$. More surprising, perhaps, is the fact that their product simplifies to c/a. These are extremely simple relationships which may be seen most easily in the equation itself when $a = 1$. The sum then simplifies further to $-b$; and the product reduces to c. Thus in the equation

$$x^2 + 7x + 12 = 0$$

the sum of the roots is -7 and their product is 12. The roots are therefore $x = -3$; $x = -4$.

This relationship will be apparent to anyone familiar with the factorization of quadratic expressions as it forms a basis for the solution of equations by factorization.

$$x^2 + 7x + 12 = 0$$
$$(x + 3)(x + 4) = 0$$

whence
$$\begin{cases} x = -3 \\ x = -4 \end{cases}$$

These roots are derived from the separate factors, and the rules for the multiplication of such factors necessarily establishes the relationships noted above. The interesting point here is that any quadratic expression may be 'factorized' provided we do not insist on real numbers as the factors – which are

$$\left(x + \frac{b - \sqrt{(b^2 - 4ac)}}{2a}\right) \text{ and } \left(x + \frac{b + \sqrt{(b^2 - 4ac)}}{2a}\right)$$

This is useful for any quadratic expression even when integral values are involved if the factors are not immediately apparent by inspection.

The relationships noted between the roots also enable us to reconstruct an equation from given roots without having to multiply the factors together. If, for example, the roots of an equation are $(2 + \sqrt{5})$ and $(2 - \sqrt{5})$ then their sum is 4 and their product is -1. Assuming that the first term of the equation is x^2 then the coefficient of x is -4 and the absolute term (the one not involving x) is -1. The equation is

$$x^2 - 4x - 1 = 0$$

The process of 'completing the square' to solve a quadratic equation is the algebraic equivalent of the method employed by the Greeks, who regarded such an equation as expressing the relation between certain dimensions of a geometrical figure.

The form in which the Greeks expressed a quadratic equation was more restricted than our present-day general form. Zero had not then been thought of as a number in its own right and, if it had been, it would have been rapidly dismissed as masquerading under false pretences; and, of course, the use of letters as coefficients to generalize formulae had not been invented either. The Greeks would have expressed a particular equation such as

$$x^2 + 10x - 11 = 0$$

in a form essentially equivalent to

$$x^2 + 10x = 11$$

This may be geometrically interpreted as stating that an area of 11 square units is made up of a square (of side x) and a rectangle (of sides x and 10 units respectively). This rectangle may also itself be divided into two rectangles, each of side x and 5 units respectively; and the whole area may be arranged as an L-shaped figure, or gnomon, as in Fig. 29.

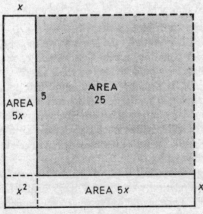

Fig. 29

A small square, of side 5 units, may be fitted into the L-shape (as shown by the shaded part) so as to form a larger square, of side $(x + 5)$ units. This is how the Greeks 'completed the square'.

The area of the L-shaped figure is 11 square units; the area of the small square is 25 square units, so the area of the larger square is 36 square units. The side of this square is $(x + 5)$ units, whence x must be 1 unit.

Heron of Alexandria had already reduced the solution of geometrical problems to a numerical calculation. One of his problems was: 'Given the sum of the diameter, perimeter and area of a circle, to find each of them.' If the sum of the quantities representing these separate dimensions, in suitable units, is 212; and d is the diameter; then assuming $\pi = 3\frac{1}{7}$ the equation is

$$\frac{11}{14}d^2 + \frac{29d}{7} = 212$$

Heron multiplied throughout by 154 so as to make the first term a perfect square, thus transforming the equation to

$$(11d)^2 + 58.11d = 32,648$$

and then, by adding 29^2 to each side he arrived at the result

$$(11d + 29)^2 = 33,489$$

whence d is shown to be 14 units.

This method is essentially the same as we might follow today for a particular equation, except that instead of multiplying by 154 throughout, we would divide by $(11 \div 14)$ so as to make the first term d^2. It is not, of course, equivalent to the modern generalized algebraic method; but in case this might tend to give us an unworthy feeling of superiority, we have to take note of the apparently solid evidence of Babylonian antiquities that a formula very similar to ours must already have been known nearly four thousand years ago.

The purely geometrical method could give only one root – a positive one – but that was all the Greeks would have asked of their geometry. They would not have accepted a negative root as being meaningful, and they had never even dreamed of imaginary numbers. Furthermore, they would not have entertained the possibility of two positive roots because a necessary condition for such a result is that, where a is positive, in the equation

$$ax^2 + bx + c = 0$$

then b must be negative and c must be positive. Thus the equation

$$x^2 - 7x + 12 = 0$$

has the positive roots $x = 3$; $x = 4$. But this equation is in modern form. The Greek form would have been equivalent to

$$x^2 - 7x = -12$$

which would then have been patently absurd as purporting to imply a minus area.

Every quadratic equation has exactly two roots, a property which is a special case of a more general property. An equation of the nth degree has exactly n roots – no more and no less. This is called the Fundamental Theorem of Algebra and was proved by the youthful Gauss while still in his early twenties. Its proof depends upon the fact that an expression of the nth degree has n 'factors' and there is one root of the equation for each such factor.

The proof that a quadratic equation cannot have *more* than two roots is a particularly elegant example of the *reductio ad absurdum* method. It is first assumed that there are three roots, all different, say A, B, and C. Each of these roots satisfy the same equation, so

$$aA^2 + bA + c = 0 \qquad \ldots\ldots \quad \text{(i)}$$
$$aB^2 + bB + c = 0 \qquad \ldots\ldots \quad \text{(ii)}$$
$$aC^2 + bC + c = 0 \qquad \ldots\ldots \quad \text{(iii)}$$

By subtracting (ii) from (i):

$$a(A^2 - B^2) + b(A - B) = 0$$

So

$$a(A + B) + b = 0 \text{ (after dividing by A} - \text{B)} \quad \ldots\ldots \quad \text{(iv)}$$

it being noted that $(A - B)$ itself cannot be zero since A and B are assumed to be different.

Again, by subtracting (iii) from (ii):

$$a(B + C) + b = 0 \qquad \ldots\ldots \quad \text{(v)}$$

Finally, by subtracting (v) from (iv):

$$a(A - C) = 0$$

but this is impossible since a (the coefficient of x^2) is not zero; and $(A - C)$ cannot be zero since the roots A and C were assumed to be different. The original assumption thus leads to a contradiction.

A cubic equation has three roots, a quartic (or biquadratic) equation has four roots, and so on. General solutions of cubic and quartic equations had already been discovered by the sixteenth century. These, like those of quadratic equations, were expressed in terms of the coefficients of the equations, and it was natural that mathematicians should look for similar formulae for higher degree equations. It was eventually proved by Abel and Galois, quite independently of each other, that fifth and higher degree equations could not in fact be solved generally by reference to their coefficients.

As early as the twelfth century Omar Khayyam had classified the various types of cubic equations and, although he had not found a general solution, he nevertheless managed to solve some particular types. The discovery of the general method did not occur until the beginning of the sixteenth century.

Discovery is one thing; publication is another, and the circumstances of the publication of the cubic solution is something of a *cause célèbre*. Details vary in different accounts, but the generally accepted story refers the solution to the outcome of a challenge between two mathematicians.

Antonio del Fiore of Bologna had learned from his master, Scipio del Ferro, of a particular solution to the cubic of form $x^3 + bx = c$. Niccolo Fontana, known as Tartaglia (the stammerer), a teacher of mathematics in Venice, claimed to be able to solve another type of cubic of the form $x^3 + bx^2 = c$. It appears that Fiore, doubting the substance of Tartaglia's claim, challenged him to a mathematical contest in which each would set the other thirty problems to solve.

Tartaglia, having accepted the proposed duel of the cubics, wisely set about the sharpening of his attack. This he did by finding a general solution for all forms of cubic equations. He was thus able to solve all the equations proposed by Fiore. He himself posed problems which involved the solution of the second type mentioned above and Fiore, knowing the solution only to the first type of equation, could not solve any of Tartaglia's equations at all.

At about the time of this contest a third mathematician Girolamo Cardan was in the course of writing his *Ars Magna*. Wishing to include a note on cubic equations, he approached Tartaglia for details of his solution. After some intrigue in which he was lured to Milan by some false pretence, Tartaglia, who had at first refused to communicate the solution, finally succumbed to Cardan's blandishments upon the latter solemnly swearing not to reveal it.

Cardan, however, promptly included the solution in his book, issued in 1545, saying that Tartaglia had given him the result and that he himself had had to establish the actual proof. This, having regard to the complicated structure of the result, certainly seems improbable. Cardan's explanation was not made more acceptable by his reputation for scandalous intrigues, but the publication of the solution successfully identified it with his name so that it has ever since been known as Cardan's Solution.

There are many unusual stories connected with Cardan who even at his birth was, according to his own report, born more dead than alive and had to be revived in a bath of warm wine. One story in particular, if true, points an appropriately ironic moral. It is said that after many vicissitudes he conceived a passion for astrology and took up a post in the Papal Court at Rome. Here, however, he seems to have overplayed his hand since, having foretold that he would die on a certain date, the only way in which he could maintain his astrological reputation was to commit suicide.

The general form of the cubic equation is

$$x^3 + ax^2 + bx + c = 0 \qquad \ldots \ldots \quad \text{(i)}$$

which may be reduced to the form

$$x^3 + bx + c = 0 \qquad \ldots \ldots \quad \text{(ii)}$$

by a subtle but simple operation. As in a quadratic equation, the sum of the roots of a cubic equation may be shown to be equal to the coefficient of the second term with its sign changed. Thus the roots of equation (i) sum to $-a$.

If we add $a/3$ to each of the three roots of this equation, thus forming a new equation, then the sum of the roots of this new equation will be $-a + 3\,(a/3) = 0$. So the coefficient of x^2 in the new equation is zero; that is the second term will in effect disappear, leaving an equation in the form (ii) shown above. If we can solve this second equation we shall also be able to calculate the roots of the original equation since these are each $a/3$ less than the respective roots of the second equation.

Cardan's Solution was basically a geometric one. He proposed that two cubes could be identified such that (i) the product of their respective edges is $b/3$; and (ii) the difference between the length of the edges of the two cubes is C; and that x will be equal to the difference between these edge lengths. The geometrical justification of this method given by Cardan is rather involved; the algebraic equivalent is easier to follow. For simplicity's sake this has been condensed in what follows and we restrict our attention to just one of the roots of the equation.

The first step is to demonstrate the proposition; the second step is to show how the subsequent determination of the root is effected.

Let the selected cubes be u^3 and v^3 so that their sides are u and v respectively. Then by hypothesis

(i) $$uv = \tfrac{1}{3}\,b; \text{ or } b = 3\,uv$$

(ii) $$u^3 - v^3 = C$$

Substitute for b and c in the equation $x^3 + bx = C$

Then $$x^3 + 3\,uv(x) = u^3 - v^3$$

If, as claimed, $x = u - v$; then substituting for x:

$$(u - v)^3 + 3\,uv(u - v) = u^3 - v^3$$

and indeed the expression on the left-hand side of the equation does simplify to the expression on the right-hand side. This does not explain how we find that x does equal $(u - v)$ in the first place, but it is sufficient here.

From (i)
$$u^3v^3 = \left(\frac{b}{3}\right)^3 \qquad \ldots\ldots \text{ (iii)}$$

So
$$v^3 = \left(\frac{b}{3}\right)^3 \div u^3$$

But from (ii)
$$u^3 - v^3 = C$$

So
$$u^6 - u^3v^3 = Cu^3$$

and from (iii)
$$u^6 - \left(\frac{b}{3}\right)^3 = Cu^3$$

So
$$(u^3)^2 - Cu^3 - \left(\frac{b}{3}\right)^3 = 0$$

This is a quadratic equation in u^3; so u^3 and therefore also u may be identified from this equation. We can then find v by substituting for u in equation (i). Then, since $x = u - v$, so x can also be identified.

The formula which results, showing x directly in terms of b and c, is a complicated one. The formula for biquadratic equations is even more so. In fact the calculations involved are so tedious that mathematicians often settle for an approximate numerical solution in the same way as they have to be thus satisfied in respect of equations of higher degree. It is possible to obtain approximate values of real roots to any required degree of accuracy.

The equation $x^3 - 2x - 5 = 0$ has only one real root, the others being imaginary. A simple approximation method, based on an initial trial and error operation, proceeds as follows.

When $x = 2$, the value of the expression $(x^3 - 2x - 5)$ is -1. When $x = 3$ the value of the expression is 16. Provided the equation has a real root, and it does (there are ways of checking this before we start), then it is evident that the value of the root lies between 2 and 3 and that it is closer to the former than to the latter value. A closer approximation is given by the value $x = 2 \cdot 1$; the value of the expression then being $0 \cdot 061$. Consequently x

must be still less than 2·1. On the other hand, the value $x = 2.09$ gives the value of the function as approx. -0.0507. So x must lie between 2·09 and 2·1. Continuing in this way we can get as close as we like to the required root value.

This method may, however, be bettered by a geometrical method based on the properties of right-angled triangles and their trigonometrical ratios. If we could draw the curve of the function $y = x^3 - 2x - 5$ with precision we could of course read off, or interpolate, from this curve the value of x when $y = 0$. This would effectively identify the root of the equation, but it is easier to talk about curves than it is to draw them.

If, however, we confine our attention to a very small part of the curve we may regard this as approximating very closely to a straight line – the smaller the part of the curve, so the closer the approximation would be. The part of the curve between the values $x = 2.09$ and $x = 2.1$ is very small indeed, and may be taken as approximating to the straight line DA (greatly magnified for the purpose of demonstration) in Fig. 30. At point A, $x =$

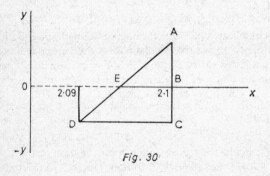

Fig. 30

2·1; $y = 0.061$. At point D, $x = 2.09$; $y = -0.0507$ approx. These values have been obtained by the previous approximation method.

The value of y at D is negative, this point being below the x axis. So FD $= -0.0507$. DC is drawn parallel to the x axis: AC is drawn parallel to the y axis. Then BC $=$ FD $= -0.0507$.

The value of y at A is 0·061; so AB = 0·061. If we now disregard the axes then the triangle ACD is a right-angled triangle in which

$$AC = AB + BC = 0·061 + 0·0507 = 0·1117$$
$$DC = \qquad\qquad\qquad 2·1 - 2·09 = 0·01$$

so the gradient of

DA (that is, the tangent of angle CDA) = AC ÷ DC = 11·17.

The triangle ABE is also a right-angled triangle which by construction is similar to triangle ACD. The gradient of EA is therefore the same as the gradient of DA; it is therefore also 11·17.

This gradient is represented by the ratio AB/EB. By construction AB = 0·061. EB = 2·1 − Z, where Z represents the value of x at E; this being the point where the curve cuts the x axis and where accordingly y = 0. So

$$x = \frac{AB}{EB} = \frac{0·061}{2·1 - Z} = 11·17$$

and this equation can be solved to provide the value of Z as approx. 2·0945. This is a very close approximation since the value of the expression $(x^3 - 2x - 5)$ is then approx. −0·0006, which is probably as near zero as may be required. If it is not close enough, the whole procedure can be repeated in respect of the part of the curve between the values $x = 2·1$; and $x = 2·0945$.

The method affords a resourceful example of the application of trigonometrical principles, by way of co-ordinate geometry and Pythagoras' Theorem, to a geometrical equivalent of a purely algebraic equation, and it throws an illuminating spotlight upon one of the many points of contact between different branches of mathematics.

The equations so far considered have all been in one unknown variable only. In order to obtain general solutions for equations in n unknowns, it is necessary to have a set of n related equations which are all satisfied by the same values of the unknowns. In the equation

$$3x + 2y = 17$$

there is always a value of y for every value of x. There is an infinite number of possible solutions and this paradoxically offers no solution at all except in a general form.

If, however, we have *two* equations – showing in effect two different relationships between the same two unknown variables – then a unique solution is possible. Thus with the additional equation

$$4x + 3y = 23$$

we can solve the two equations simultaneously to show that $x = 5$; $y = 1$. These kinds of equations will find their niche in the next chapter.

In some practical applications it may be possible to obtain only one equation, but if the roots are restricted in some way, it may be possible either to identify them or at least to limit the possible number of solutions.

Equations which admit of an infinite number of solutions if no restrictions are imposed are called indeterminate equations. If the solutions are restricted to rational numbers, or more specifically, to positive integral numbers, the equations are called Diophantine equations.

Diophantus was a mathematician in Alexandria in about the third century A.D., but little else is known about him as a person, except his supposed age at the time of his death. Tradition has handed down a problem which purports to show his age in the form of an equation – his boyhood lasted for one-sixth of his life; his beard grew after one-twelfth more; after one-seventh more he married; his son was born 5 years later; the son lived to one-half of Diophantus' age, and Diophantus died 4 years after his son.

If x was Diophantus' age at his death, then

$$\tfrac{1}{6}x + \tfrac{1}{12}x + \tfrac{1}{7}x + 5 + \tfrac{1}{2}x + 4 = x$$

and this can be simplified to show that Diophantus was 84 when he died.

Diophantus applied himself to finding ways of solving 'restricted' equations and, in particular, he restricted his solutions to positive integers. He did not accept the possibility of negative numbers, and imaginary numbers had then not even been dreamed about.

It might be thought that to find positive integers to satisfy the equation

$$7x + 12y = 220 \qquad \dots \dots \text{ (i)}$$

would require a trial and error method and a great deal of luck. This is not so. There is a very simple method. The first step is to divide the equation throughout by the lowest coefficient. In equation (i) the lowest coefficient is 7. We then obtain the equation

$$x + \frac{12y}{7} = \frac{220}{7}$$

This is the same as

$$x + y + \frac{5y}{7} = 31 + \frac{3}{7}$$

or

$$x + y + \frac{5y - 3}{7} = 31 \qquad \dots \dots \text{ (ii)}$$

Since x and y are to be integers, then so also must $(5y - 3)/7$ be an integer. Multiply this by 3 so as to make the coefficient of y greater by 1 than a multiple of 7. This gives us $(15y - 9)/7$ which must again be an integer. Again, divide out by 7.

$$\frac{15y - 9}{7} = 2y - 1 + \frac{y - 2}{7}$$

That is, 7 divided into $(15y - 9)$ gives an integer quotient and a remainder which must also be an integer. Let this remainder

$$\frac{y - 2}{7} = S$$

then

$$y - 2 = 7S$$

or

$$y = 7S + 2$$

Substituting this value in equation (ii) gives

$$x + (7S + 2) + (5S + 1) = 31$$

So

$$x = 28 - 12S \qquad \dots \dots \text{ (iii)}$$

Equation (i) is therefore satisfied by any integral value of x found by substituting any integral value of S in equation (iii). This still implies an infinite number of solutions, but it will be observed that x will be *negative* for any value of S greater than 2.

Accordingly, the solutions for *positive* integral values of x, are restricted to three only, that is: $S = 0$, 1 and 2; whence $x = 28$, 16 and 4; and $y = 2$, 9 and 16 respectively.

This method is of general application although the results obtained may not always be so conveniently restricted as in this example. It has the merit of showing the number of different ways in which integral values may be paired so as to satisfy the equation and this, in itself, is often quite an important fact to establish.

It was noted earlier that the quantity $(b^2 - 4ac)$ is defined as the discriminant of a quadratic equation of the form

$$ax^2 + bx + c = 0 \qquad \ldots\ldots \text{ (i)}$$

If for x in this equation we substitute an equivalent y expressed in terms of x we shall obtain a new equation of the form

$$Ay^2 + By + C = 0 \qquad \ldots\ldots \text{ (ii)}$$

Let
$$y = (px + q) \div (rx + s) \qquad \ldots\ldots \text{ (iii)}$$

then it may be shown that

$$B^2 - 4AC = (ps - qr)^2 (b^2 - 4ac)$$

That is, the discriminant of the transformed equation (ii) in y is the product of (a) the discriminant of the original equation (i) in x, and (b) an expression which depends only upon the coefficients in equation (iii). When the expression $(ps - qr)^2 = 1$; then the two discriminants are exactly equal.

The discriminants of the equation

$$x^2 + 2x + 3 = 0 \qquad \ldots\ldots \text{ (i)}$$

and of the transformed equation

$$3y^2 - 16y + 22 = 0 \qquad \ldots\ldots \text{ (ii)}$$

obtained by setting

$$y = \frac{3x + 5}{x + 2} \text{ whence } x = \frac{5 - 2y}{y - 3}$$

are respectively

(i) $\qquad\qquad\qquad 2^2 - 4.1.3 = -8$

(ii) $\qquad\qquad\qquad 16^2 - 4.3.22 = -8$

This is a particular example of a general property. The discriminant of every equation always reappears as a factor of the discriminant of the transformed equation.

The discovery of this property was an important step in the development of the concept of invariance, which in general is concerned with the unvarying nature of certain quantities. It is not difficult to appreciate the potential significance of such a concept in ascertaining which quantities, among all others, retain an invariant property when, as Kipling might have said, all around are losing theirs.

8. Simultaneous Equations and Matrices

Simultaneous equations involve the same unknown quantities and are satisfied by the same values of those quantities. They are of interest because of the surprising facility with which many of them may be solved and the ingenuity called forth in dealing with the less simple ones. They have a wide range of applications, from the solving of humble magazine problems to the technicalities of linear programming, and they provide a simplified approach to the intriguing aspects of matrix theory.

It might once have seemed that, if it were not possible to solve one equation involving x and y, then it would merely double the difficulties by trying to solve two equations. Naturally this is not so. One equation might be likened to an unidentified radio signal; two equations help us to trap the relevant values of x and y much as a radio fix enables a transmitter to be located.

Two equations are better than one! This perhaps sounds more like a motto of the affluent society, but it is literally true. In general we need as many equations as there are unknown quantities to be identified. It may seem to be stating the obvious to remark that these equations must each be different one from the other, yet this caution is necessary in order to see through the disguise of any equation which masquerades as another. Each equation must in effect exhibit some different relationship between the unknown quantities, but they must at the same time be consistent with each other.

We cannot, for example, solve the equations

$$\left.\begin{array}{r} 2x + 3y = 7 \\ 4x + 6y = 10 \end{array}\right\}$$

because these are inconsistent. If $2x + 3y = 7$; then $4x + 6y = 14$. If the first equation correctly states the relationship between x and y, then the second equation cannot also be correct.

Nor can we solve the equations

$$3x + 4y = 12$$
$$6x + 8y = 24$$

for, although they are consistent, the second equation tells us nothing that the first equation has not already told us. Each side of the second equation is exactly twice as great as the respective side of the first equation. These equations have an infinite number of solutions since x is not restricted in any way and, for every value of x, there will also be a value of y.

Our ability or inability to solve sets of simultaneous equations can sometimes easily be demonstrated by drawing the curves of y expressed in terms of x. If the curves obtained from the separate equations intersect, but are not coincident, then these equations may be solved but otherwise they cannot. There is, however, an algebraic method of checking before we start whether a set of simultaneous equations can be solved. This will be shown later in the chapter; meanwhile, unless otherwise remarked upon, our examples will be restricted to examples which can be solved.

There are many different ways of tackling simultaneous equations and they are more suitable or less suitable for a specific set of equations according to the structure of the particular equations. There is, therefore, some scope for ingenuity and initiative in selecting the best method.

One general method, which is an analogue of the solution of equations by the intersecting of curves of functions, is to detect the explicit functional relationship between the unknown quantities. In the equations

$$3x + 7y = 27 \qquad \ldots\ldots \quad \text{(i)}$$
$$5x + 2y = 16 \qquad \ldots\ldots \quad \text{(ii)}$$

we first state y in terms of x and then equate the results from the two equations. Thus

(i) $\qquad\qquad y = \frac{1}{7}(27 - 3x)$

(ii) $\qquad\qquad y = \frac{1}{2}(16 - 5x)$

Equating these two expressions and simplifying the resultant equation gives the value $x = 2$. Substituting this value in either of the two original equations then gives the value $y = 3$.

This method is unnecessarily protracted for simple cases and it is often possible to use a much simpler elimination process. This may involve multiplication as in the equations

$$\left.\begin{array}{l} 2x + 7y = 48 \\ 4x + 5y = 42 \end{array}\right\} \qquad \ldots\ldots \text{ (i)} \atop \ldots\ldots \text{ (ii)}$$

Multiply (i) by 2; $4x + 14y = 96$ $\ldots\ldots$ (iii)
Subtract (ii) from (iii) $9y = 54$; whence
$$y = 6$$
The value of x may then be found as $x = 3$.

It may sometimes be necessary to multiply both equations.

$$\left.\begin{array}{l} 2x + 5y = 23 \\ 3x + 4y = 24 \end{array}\right\} \qquad \ldots\ldots \text{ (i)} \atop \ldots\ldots \text{ (ii)}$$

Multiply (i) by 3; $6x + 15y = 69$ $\ldots\ldots$ (iii)
Multiply (ii) by 2; $6x + 8y = 48$ $\ldots\ldots$ (iv)
Subtract (iv) from (iii) $7y = 21$; whence
$$y = 3 \text{ (and } x = 4)$$

In this example equation (i) was multiplied by the x coefficient in equation (ii); and similarly the latter was multiplied by the x coefficient in the former. This makes it possible to eliminate x by subtraction. We could, instead, have eliminated y by a similar operation. If the coefficients are large, however, it is only necessary to build up transformed equations so that each of the coefficients of x in these is equal to the lowest common multiple of coefficients of x in the original equations. Thus the equations

$$\left.\begin{array}{l} 33x + 2y = 113 \\ 22x + 6y = 108 \end{array}\right\} \text{ become } \left\{\begin{array}{l} 66x + 4y = 226 \\ 66x + 18y = 324 \end{array}\right.$$

It is not always necessary to multiply. Elimination may be effected by a simple subtraction or addition as in the following two examples.

$$\begin{array}{ll} 5x + 2y = 24 & \qquad 2x + 5y = 11 \\ 3x + 2y = 16 & \qquad 5x - 5y = 10 \end{array}$$

$$\begin{array}{ll} (subtract)\ 2x = 8 & \quad (add)\ 7x = 21 \end{array}$$

A more general method based on multiplication actually involves the cross-multiplication of the coefficients. In its form of application this method appears to enjoy an element of number magic but, in fact, it really only states the multiplication principle in a form of mathematical shorthand. It is best demonstrated with literal coefficients. Let the two equations be

$$ax + by = u$$
$$cx + dy = v$$

then by multiplying a by d; and c by b; that is, cross-multiplying the coefficients on the left side thus

and also forming the products cu, du, av, and bv thus

it can be shown that $(ad - bc)x = du - bv$
and $\qquad\qquad (bc - ad)y = cu - av$

whence $\qquad x = \dfrac{du - bv}{ad - bc}$ and $y = \dfrac{cu - av}{bc - ad}$

If then the equations are

$$2x + 3y = 6$$
$$5x + 9y = 3$$

then $x = (9.6 - 3.3) \div (2.9 - 3.5) = 45 \div 3 \qquad = 15$
and $y = (5.6 - 2.3) \div (3.5 - 2.9) = 24 \div (-3) = -8$

The quantity $(ad - bc)$ which appears as the denominator in the expression for x is an extremely important one. It is called a determinant and provides a link with matrix theory.

Matrices introduce new pathways in mathematics, for although they follow certain of the rules which were once accepted as absolutely inviolable and essential to the inner cohesion of mathematics, nevertheless they have some rules of their own. They can be added and subtracted. They cannot be divided out directly by other matrices, and although they can be multiplied this latter operation differs from the ordinary multiplication of arithmetic. These differences will soon become apparent.

A matrix is an array or rectangular pattern of quantities, and the latter are called the elements of the matrix. The array is enclosed within brackets to indicate that it is the pattern of the matrix – that is the relative positions of the elements – which is of primary importance. The elements will, of course, have an individual significance according to the type of problem under consideration, but for the purposes of matrix operations the property of an element in which we are particularly interested is that which derives from its membership of a set of elements.

Matrices, like most things in life, come in all sizes. Here we shall deal with the simpler matrices. This

$$\begin{pmatrix} 1 & 3 \\ 3 & 4 \end{pmatrix}$$

is a 2 × 2 matrix, so-called because it has 2 rows and 2 columns of elements.

The addition of two matrices is effected by adding in pairs the corresponding elements from the respective matrices to form a new matrix. Thus to add the matrix

$$\begin{pmatrix} 2 & 1 \\ 5 & 1 \end{pmatrix}$$

to the first matrix shown above the result is

$$\begin{pmatrix} 1+2 & 3+1 \\ 3+5 & 4+1 \end{pmatrix} \text{ or } \begin{pmatrix} 3 & 4 \\ 8 & 5 \end{pmatrix}$$

Subtraction is carried out by a reverse process

$$\begin{pmatrix} 1-2 & 3-1 \\ 3-5 & 4-1 \end{pmatrix} \text{ or } \begin{pmatrix} -1 & 2 \\ -2 & 3 \end{pmatrix}$$

The multiplication of a matrix by a single number is effected quite simply by multiplying each element by that number. Thus

$$4 \text{ times} \begin{pmatrix} 2 & 1 \\ 5 & 1 \end{pmatrix} = \begin{pmatrix} 8 & 4 \\ 20 & 4 \end{pmatrix}$$

The solution of simultaneous equations, however, requires the multiplication of one matrix by another. This is a more complicated operation altogether. It is not merely a matter of multiplying together the corresponding elements in the separate matrices. The product of two matrices is built up as

$$\begin{pmatrix} a & b \\ c & d \end{pmatrix}\begin{pmatrix} e & f \\ g & h \end{pmatrix} = \begin{pmatrix} ae+bg & af+bh \\ ce+dg & cf+dh \end{pmatrix} = \begin{pmatrix} p & q \\ r & s \end{pmatrix}$$

so that

$$\begin{pmatrix} 2 & 1 \\ 5 & 1 \end{pmatrix}\begin{pmatrix} 1 & 3 \\ 3 & 4 \end{pmatrix} = \begin{pmatrix} 2+3 & 6+4 \\ 5+3 & 15+4 \end{pmatrix} = \begin{pmatrix} 5 & 10 \\ 8 & 19 \end{pmatrix}$$

This process may be explained in more detail: Let the first and second matrices be lettered A and B respectively, and the product matrix be lettered C.

Take the first row (a, b) of matrix A and the first column (e, g) of matrix B. Form the products ae and bg, and add these to give the first element in the first row of matrix C.

Next take the same row (a, b) of A and the second column (f, h) of B. Form the products af and bh and add these to give the second element in the first row of C.

In the same way take the second row (c, d) of A and associate this in turn first with the first column (e, g) of B and then with the second column (f, h) of B. The respective products are then added to produce the elements $(ce + dg)$ and $(cf + dh)$ as the elements in the first and second places in the second row of C.

It may be asked why the elements are multiplied and their products added in this very particular manner. The simple answer, if it *is* an answer, is that this is a special process designed for a specific purpose, and this purpose can be fulfilled by matrix theory only if the special procedure is followed. This question really arises only because of the unfortunate use of the word 'multiplication' to describe this process. This is not a simple arithmetical multiplication and would have been better called matriculation.

A matrix is a set of elements which are related in some particular way; and the process, which is called multiplication, in effect comprises a number of successive calculations to provide a product matrix which may be regarded as the resultant of the relationship between the elements of one matrix and the elements of another.

Since this does not involve a simple multiplication in the arithmetic sense, it is less surprising that it does not obey all the rules of arithmetic. There is no reason why it should; and neither does it! In arithmetic the products 3×4 and 4×3 are equal, as also is the same result generalized in the notation of elementary algebra as

$$ab = ba$$

Multiplication in this sense is said to be commutative in that the order of multiplication is immaterial.

Matrix multiplication is *not* commutative. Matrix A multiplied by matrix B does not produce the same result as matrix B multiplied by matrix A. The order of multiplication is thus of great importance. In any expression for the multiplication of matrices, the multiplier matrix is always shown first. In the multiplication shown above, matrix B was multiplied by matrix A. The multiplication of matrix A by matrix B gives the quite different result

$$\begin{pmatrix} 1 & 3 \\ 3 & 4 \end{pmatrix} \begin{pmatrix} 2 & 1 \\ 5 & 1 \end{pmatrix} = \begin{pmatrix} 2+15 & 1+3 \\ 6+20 & 3+4 \end{pmatrix} = \begin{pmatrix} 17 & 4 \\ 26 & 7 \end{pmatrix}$$

This idea is not always easy to grasp when first encountered. Nevertheless the concept of order is of prime importance in many mathematical contexts. The order of digits in any numeral, for example, is unique for the quantity represented. If the order of digits in the numeral 123 is altered in any way, a different quantity (e.g. 321, 132 etc.) will result.

A similar example may be observed in the atomic representation of isomeric organic substances. The term isomerism denotes the phenomenon of two or more different substances whose molecules consist of the same number of the same atoms, and it apparently reflects the different arrangements of these atoms within the respective molecules.

The phenomenon was first observed by Wohler in 1828 in connection with ammonium cyanate and urea each of which has the same ultimate chemical composition, CON_2H_4 but different atomic arrangements.

$$NH_4 \cdot O \cdot CN \qquad\qquad NH_2 \cdot CO \cdot NH_2$$
$$\text{Ammonium cyanate} \qquad\qquad \text{Urea}$$

The analogy between chemical formulae and mathematical numeral symbols is not complete since differing numerals represent quantities of quite different magnitudes whereas isomers, while having different atomic structures and different characteristics, consist of the same ultimate constituent elements in exactly the same proportions.

This analogy may, however, be pressed to point a moral of immense significance as to the stultifying dangers inherent in too great a reliance upon analogy!

Wöhler was astonished to obtain crystals of urea from a solution of ammonium cyanate because he had thus, in a laboratory process, produced a substance which had always hitherto been regarded as distinctively related only to animal life. The spark of life had always been thought to be an essential catalyst for the production of an organic substance such as this.

In mathematics too, and in algebra in particular, it had for centuries been supposed that the commutative property of multiplication extended invariably to every other kind of operation which appeared to have all the characteristics of multiplication. As with the chemistry of living matter, it was not seen how the truth could be otherwise. Today, indeed, there are whole new abstract non-commutative algebras.

All this is easier to appreciate in retrospect. Hamilton, who in 1843 was the first to conceive the propriety of non-commutative algebras, was so overjoyed that he is said to have carved some appropriate formulae on a stone bridge where he happened to be when the inspiration smote him. Certainly he had reason to celebrate. Wohler seems to have made his discovery by accident, whereas Hamilton's discovery was a positive personal one achieved after years of hard thinking and frustration · in the wilderness known only too well by research scientists.

A matrix of particular interest is

$$\begin{pmatrix} 1 & 0 \\ 0 & 1 \end{pmatrix}$$

which acts in matrix multiplication rather as the number 1 acts upon other numbers in ordinary multiplication in that it leaves a multiplied matrix unchanged. It is called the unit or identity matrix.

Also of importance are inverse matrices. They are not unlike the reciprocals of numbers in that a matrix multiplied by its inverse matrix will produce the unit matrix. The inverse of a 2 × 2 matrix

$$\begin{pmatrix} a & b \\ c & d \end{pmatrix}$$

is obtained by (i) interchanging the top left and bottom right elements and (ii) changing the sign of the other two elements, and (iii) dividing throughout by $(ad - bc)$. The inverse then is

$$\frac{1}{ad - bc} \begin{pmatrix} d & -b \\ -c & a \end{pmatrix}$$

This is relatively simple for a 2 × 2 matrix although not for other matrices. In fact this is a deceptive simplicity. The method employed here is a short cut justified only by a much longer process which is applicable to matrices of all dimensions.

In the above formula there reappears a quantity of the form $(ad - bc)$ which we first noted in connection with simultaneous equations a few pages back. The general preliminaries over, we may now proceed to apply matrix theory to these equations.

The inverse of $\begin{pmatrix} 3 & 5 \\ 1 & 2 \end{pmatrix}$ is $\begin{pmatrix} 2 & -5 \\ -1 & 3 \end{pmatrix}$

it being noted that in this particular case $(ad - bc) = 1$.

There is one important condition attached to the multiplication of matrices – the number of columns in the first or multiplying matrix must be the same as the number of rows in the second or multiplied matrix. The product matrix has as many rows as the first matrix and as many columns as the second matrix. Thus

$$\begin{pmatrix} 3 & 5 \\ 1 & 2 \end{pmatrix}\begin{pmatrix} 1 \\ 3 \end{pmatrix} = \begin{pmatrix} 3.1 + 5.3 \\ 1.1 + 2.3 \end{pmatrix} = \begin{pmatrix} 18 \\ 7 \end{pmatrix} \quad \ldots\ldots \quad \text{(i)}$$

Here we have a matrix with only one column but with two rows.

The significance of the above result is revealed if we substitute x and y for the elements in the second matrix. Thus

$$\begin{pmatrix} 3 & 5 \\ 1 & 2 \end{pmatrix}\begin{pmatrix} x \\ y \end{pmatrix} = \begin{pmatrix} 3x + 5y \\ x + 2y \end{pmatrix} \quad \ldots\ldots \quad \text{(ii)}$$

It should be observed that the product matrix still has only one column. The expression $3x + 5y$ represents only one element and we cannot simplify it further because its two terms are functions of different unknown quantities.

If, however, we reverse the substitution – instead of substituting x and y for 1 and 3, we substitute 1 and 3 for x and y respectively – then the matrix operation (ii) is identical to matrix operation (i) and for these values of x and y the product matrix of (ii) simplifies to the product matrix of (i); that is

$$\begin{pmatrix} 3x + 5y \\ x + 2y \end{pmatrix} = \begin{pmatrix} 18 \\ 7 \end{pmatrix} \quad \ldots\ldots \quad \text{(iii)}$$

One further property of matrices, essential to their application to simultaneous equations, is that one matrix is 'equal' to another if, and only if, it is in fact identical to the other – that is they have the same elements in the same array. So the two matrices above are equal only if

$$3x + 5y = 18$$
$$x + 2y = 7$$

for the same value of x and y throughout.

Accordingly we have derived a set of simultaneous equations out of a matrix operation. To do so we had to know the values of x and y. To solve simultaneous equations we merely reverse the process. For the equations

$$2x + 3y = 6$$
$$5x + 9y = 3$$

we express these in a matrix form equivalent to the form in (ii) as completed by (iii) above:

$$\begin{pmatrix} 2 & 3 \\ 5 & 9 \end{pmatrix} \begin{pmatrix} x \\ y \end{pmatrix} = \begin{pmatrix} 6 \\ 3 \end{pmatrix} \qquad \ldots\ldots \text{(iv)}$$

To obtain the values of x and y we must eliminate the first matrix; that is to say we must multiply it by its inverse so that it will produce the unit matrix; at the same time the product matrix above must also be multiplied in the same way.

The value of $(ad - bc)$ in this instance is $18 - 15 = 3$. So the inverse of the first matrix above, formed as noted previously in this chapter, is

$$\frac{1}{3} \begin{pmatrix} 9 & -3 \\ -5 & 2 \end{pmatrix}$$

Multiplying both sides of the above matrix relationship (iv) by the inverse matrix transforms it to

$$\begin{pmatrix} x \\ y \end{pmatrix} = \frac{1}{3} \begin{pmatrix} 9 & -3 \\ -5 & 2 \end{pmatrix} \begin{pmatrix} 6 \\ 3 \end{pmatrix}$$

$$= \frac{1}{3} \begin{pmatrix} 45 \\ -24 \end{pmatrix} = \begin{pmatrix} 15 \\ -8 \end{pmatrix}$$

These two matrices will be equal only if they are identical; that is only if: $x = 15$; $y = -8$.

Thus are the equations solved and the facility with which this is accomplished suggests that the method must have been tailored for this specific purpose. Yet this is not so. As so often happens in mathematical applications the fitting is not so much a made-to-measure as a ready-to-wear one.

The first requirement in the above process is to form the inverse of the coefficient matrix. A factor of this is the reciprocal of the quantity $(ad - bc)$. This can be any value depending only on the values of the coefficients involved in any particular set of equations. What is the outcome when this quantity is equal to zero?

There is no outcome at all! If $ad - bc = 0$; then we cannot of course form a meaningful inverse matrix and neither is it possible to solve the equations for unique values of x and y at all by any means whatever. For if $ad = bc$, then also a is to c as b is to d, so that each of the coefficients in the second equation is the same multiple of the respective coefficients in the first equation. The equations are therefore of the form:

$$\left. \begin{array}{l} ax + by = c \\ max + mby = mc \end{array} \right\}$$

and the information in the first equation, as to a particular relationship between x and y, is merely repeated in the second equation.

It is always possible, therefore, to check whether simultaneous equations are in fact soluble merely by calculating the value of $(ad - bc)$. This quantity is called the determinant of the matrix and may be written as

$$\begin{vmatrix} a & b \\ c & d \end{vmatrix}$$

the straight lines indicating that this is a determinant. This is a quantity, not a set of elements, and is written in this way merely by way of mathematical expedience.

It is interesting to note that the determinant of a product matrix is equal to the product of the determinants of the matrices involved in a multiplication. An example, showing two matrices and their respective determinants, follows:

$$\text{Matrices:} \quad \begin{pmatrix} 2 & 1 \\ 5 & 1 \end{pmatrix} \begin{pmatrix} 1 & 3 \\ 3 & 4 \end{pmatrix} = \begin{pmatrix} 5 & 10 \\ 8 & 19 \end{pmatrix}$$

Determinants: $(2-5) \times (4-9) = (95-80)$
or $\qquad (-3) \times (-5) = (15)$

The use of matrices for the solution of equations is of great practical utility and provides a reasonably simple introduction to general matrix theory. A more elementary introduction with an intriguing appeal outside mathematics is often effected by showing suggested usages of matrices in code messages.

A simple numerical code may be built up as

A B C D E F G H ... Y Z
1 2 3 4 5 6 7 8 ... 25 0

Using this code the set of numbers 6135 would represent FACE. This can be put into matrix form which may then be multiplied by some arbitrarily chosen matrix A

$$\begin{pmatrix} 2 & 1 \\ 3 & 2 \end{pmatrix} \begin{pmatrix} 6 & 1 \\ 3 & 5 \end{pmatrix} = \begin{pmatrix} 15 & 7 \\ 24 & 13 \end{pmatrix} \text{ where A is } \begin{pmatrix} 2 & 1 \\ 3 & 2 \end{pmatrix}$$

The word FACE, represented by 6135 in the alphabet code, is thus represented by 15.7.24.13 in the matrix code. Any arbitrary multiplying matrix could be used so that there could be a different code for each day.

To decipher the code word when it is received, we merely multiply the coded matrix by the inverse matrix of A. Thus

$$\begin{pmatrix} 2 & -1 \\ -3 & 2 \end{pmatrix} \begin{pmatrix} 15 & 7 \\ 24 & 13 \end{pmatrix} = \begin{pmatrix} 6 & 1 \\ 3 & 5 \end{pmatrix}$$

This is justified because the whole process of encoding and decoding is equivalent to multiplying the message matrix by the unit matrix. To encode we multiply by A; to decode we multiply by the inverse of A.

It is, of course, necessary that the determinant of the arbitrarily chosen matrix A should not be zero; and for simplicity it would be desirable that the determinant, as in matrix A, should be equal to 1.

One apparent advantage of this form of code is that it conceals the repetition of the same letter. The word GAFF, represented by 7166 in the simple code, would become 20.8.33.15 in the matrix code

$$\begin{pmatrix} 2 & 1 \\ 3 & 2 \end{pmatrix} \begin{pmatrix} 7 & 1 \\ 6 & 6 \end{pmatrix} = \begin{pmatrix} 20 & 8 \\ 33 & 15 \end{pmatrix}$$

This successfully hides the fact that the letter F occurs twice.

There is always a danger that the coding clerk might try to multiply the matrices in the wrong order. This would naturally give a different and probably quite unintelligible message. A much greater practical disadvantage is that a computer, which can handle matrices with such manifest ease, might by a process of elimination break the code in less time than it would take to transmit the message!

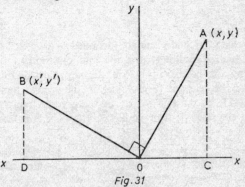

Fig. 31

A simple rotation example from geometry will illustrate one of the ways in which matrix theory can be applied to isometric problems (an isometry being a geometric transformation in which specified shapes change their positions but retain their original shapes and sizes).

In Fig. 31 the point (x, y) is represented by A and its transform

$(x'y')$ is represented by B. This transformation may be regarded as being effected by the rotation of the line OA anti-clockwise through an angle of 90° about O, the point A then coinciding with the point B.

The lines AC and BD are drawn perpendicular to the x axis thus forming the triangles OAC and BOD. These are congruent triangles since AO = BO; angles COA = DBO; and the angles ACO and ODB are right angles. Then

$$-x' = y; \text{ so } x' = -y \text{ (since OD = AC)}$$
$$\text{and} \qquad y' = \quad x \text{ (since BD = OC)}$$

These two equations can be written in the form

$$\left. \begin{array}{r} 0x - 1y = x' \\ 1x + 0y = y' \end{array} \right\}$$

and may be put into matrix form as

$$\begin{pmatrix} 0 & -1 \\ 1 & 0 \end{pmatrix} \begin{pmatrix} x \\ y \end{pmatrix} = \begin{pmatrix} x' \\ y' \end{pmatrix}$$

So the values of x' and y' may be identified as the elements of the product matrix resulting from the multiplication of the (x,y) matrix by the coefficient matrix. In any particular case we substitute the relevant (x,y) values in the second matrix and multiply this by the first matrix. If the point A represents the values $x = 3$; $y = 4$; then we have

$$\begin{pmatrix} 0 & -1 \\ 1 & 0 \end{pmatrix} \begin{pmatrix} 3 \\ 4 \end{pmatrix} = \begin{pmatrix} -4 \\ 3 \end{pmatrix}$$

by completing the multiplication. So $x' = -4$; $y' = 3$.

Another geometrical example, which has familiar applications in mechanics as well as many others, may be drawn from the parallelogram law for the addition of vectors. In mechanics this law refers to velocities and forces as well as in other contexts but these considerations can all be generalized into a treatment by vector theory.

A vector is a straight line segment which has both direction and length. In Fig. 32, $\overrightarrow{OA}$ and $\overrightarrow{OC}$ represent two vectors. Their sum is represented by $\overrightarrow{OB}$ which is the diagonal of the parallelogram ABCO. Since each vector originates at O it is defined by its end

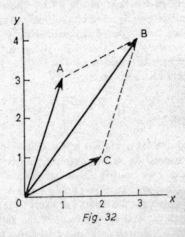

Fig. 32

point A, B or C and these points are in turn defined by their respective (x, y) values. The vectors $\overrightarrow{OA}$ and $\overrightarrow{OC}$ may be represented in matrix form by reference to their known (x, y) values. A is the point $x = 1$; $y = 3$. C is the point $x = 2$; $y = 1$. The addition of these vectors may then be effected by adding the two matrices to form a third matrix which will provide the (x, y) values of point B:

$$\begin{pmatrix} 1 \\ 3 \end{pmatrix} + \begin{pmatrix} 2 \\ 1 \end{pmatrix} = \begin{pmatrix} 3 \\ 4 \end{pmatrix}$$

$$\overrightarrow{OA} + \overrightarrow{OC} = \overrightarrow{OB}$$

So point B has the values $x = 3$; $y = 4$.

This process which defines both the length and the direction of $\overrightarrow{OB}$ with almost casual ease thus appears truly as a summing of vectors. In its application to the composition and resolution of forces, the vector $\overrightarrow{OB}$ represents the resultant of the separate forces represented by the vectors $\overrightarrow{OA}$ and $\overrightarrow{OC}$ respectively.

A final glance at the unusualness of matrix algebra reveals the apparent oddity of the zero matrix all of whose elements are zero. This 'annihilates' any matrix it multiplies rather as ordinary multiplication by zero reduces any expression to zero. Its unusual aspect, however, is revealed by the possibility that the product of two matrices, neither of which is a zero matrix, may nevertheless itself be a zero matrix.

$$\begin{pmatrix} 2 & 4 \\ -1 & -2 \end{pmatrix} \begin{pmatrix} 0 & 2 \\ 0 & -1 \end{pmatrix} = \begin{pmatrix} 0 & 0 \\ 0 & 0 \end{pmatrix}$$

This has no equivalent operation in the behaviour of ordinary numbers. The expression xy, for example, can be equal to zero only if either x or y (or both) is also equal to zero.

Only a few of the very elementary applications of matrix theory have been noted here, but the theory has a very wide utility indeed. Matrices proved of vital significance in the development of quantum mechanics as well as in other scientific theories. They are basic to the successful operation of linear programming which, after establishing restraints upon the possible range of results, then proceeds by the solution of sets of simultaneous equations to assess the respective merits of the possibilities.

All this being so, perhaps the most oddly interesting thing of all about matrices is that, when Cayley introduced them in 1858, he regarded them more as elegantly beautiful patterns. No one, he said, would ever find an application for them; but he loved them as his own. Thus does the offspring often confound its proud parent with unexpected talent.

9. Nothing but the Best

Many practical problems with which mathematics is expected to deal require the identification of a best possible or optimal value of a variable from a number of possible values. The problems are many and varied. Examples are: the greatest area within a given perimeter length; the shortest or quickest (not necessarily the same) route between two points; the greatest rectangle which may be inscribed within a given circle; the greatest volume possible of a carton constructed from a piece of cardboard; the largest beam which can be sawn from a tree trunk.

For most of these it is possible to obtain a general solution, so that the solutions of a particular problem may be achieved merely by substituting relevant values in a given formula. The greatest area which can be contained within a plane figure of given perimeter length, for example, is enclosed by a circle no matter what perimeter length is specified.

The simpler problems of this type can be handled with reasonable dispatch because of the facilities provided by the relevant equations which can be established in terms of only one independent variable. When there are two or more independent variables, the problems become much more complicated and general solutions are less easy to find. The complexity of such problems is often of a degree involving the solution of hundreds, or perhaps thousands, of sets of simultaneous equations, the best solution being subsequently selected by comparison. Here it is no longer possible to obtain a precise unique solution direct from a formula.

Mathematics itself cannot define what is best. The best result possible in one set of circumstances may not be the best in other circumstances as Atalanta, reputedly the fastest mortal on earth, found to the cost of her celibacy when she lost the race of her life by stopping to pick up the three golden apples cunningly placed in her path by her hopeful suitor. Again, the longest road is sometimes the quickest to travel and it is here essential to stipulate whether the criterion for defining an optimum value shall be minimum distance, minimum time, minimum cost or even perhaps maximum speed.

Choice between qualitative attributes is outside the scope of mathematics unless these can be measured. Mathematics can discriminate only between the measurements and often has to work within restrictions imposed from without. Consequently mathematics is not primarily concerned with the identification of optimum values as it is with maximum or minimum values which may or may not be optimal.

One of the intriguing aspects of this subject is that when we discover the solution to some general type of problem, we also often find that nature has thought of it first. Perhaps the most important principle in the early development of optics, discovered by Heron of Alexandria, is that the path of a ray of light emitted from one object and reflected back to a different object by a plane mirror is always of minimum possible length.

Another early discovery of perhaps less scientific significance but no less interest to the reader concerns the working habits of the proverbially sagacious bees. Pappus noted that, by building hexagonal cells in their honeycombs, the bees adopt a structure which enables them to store the maximum amount of honey with the minimum use of wax. There are only three different regular equilateral plane figures which can be fitted, like a mosaic, into an overall pattern so that there are no gaps left between the figures in the plane. These are the triangle, square and hexagon. Of these the bees use the figure which has the most angles.

It is to be doubted whether the bees know much about angles though, as the philosophic Winnie-the-Pooh once observed, 'you never can tell with bees', but it is certainly remarkable that they should build their honeycombs in the most economical manner, that the hexagons are all of approximately the same size and that the bees always adopt this method of building.

This is one of the fascinating by-products of mathematics. It would be wrong to assume that the bees act in this way because mathematics says it is the best way; yet the demonstration by mathematics that it really is the best way adds something to our knowledge of the bees which we could not otherwise have appreciated. There are, of course many imperfectly formed honeycombs, just as there are many badly constructed houses. It is to be hoped that each of these was intended to be near perfect, and some imperfection is perhaps to be expected of those drones who sample the ambrosia instead of storing it away.

Another example from nature suggests unexpected tendencies in the humble soap bubbles of our youth. The solid with the greatest volume relative to a given surface area is the sphere. The bubble, which consists of a very fine film of soap enclosing a certain amount of air, is forced by the tension in the film to adopt a shape which redistributes the enclosed air in such a way that the exterior of the film, and therefore also of the bubble itself, is as small as possible. So the bubble is as nearly spherical as it can make itself.

Nature sometimes finds it desirable to adopt for a specific purpose a maximum rather than a minimum surface area for a given contents value. This is important for instance in expediting certain processes in the human body. One of the functions of the red corpuscles in the blood is to act as oxygen carriers on their journey from the lungs to the other parts of the body. They fulfil this function by taking up a film of oxygen on their surfaces, so that the greater the surface area of a corpuscle so also the greater the amount of oxygen which may be ferried by a given quantity of blood. And so we find that the corpuscle is not spherical; instead it is in the shape of a biconcave disc which has about one and a half times the surface area of a sphere of equal volume.

This example can be interpreted either as a maximum best value (greatest surface for a given volume) or as a minimum best value (least volume for a given surface). One optimum implies the other; it is merely a question of which we require to take as a standard.

Many of the examples which occur in nature appear, so far as we can tell, to adopt minimum values as their criteria. So apparent was this thought to be by the physicist, de Maupertuis, that he was encouraged to enunciate his principle of least action. This asserts that nature behaves in such a way as to produce a minimum value for the quantities involved in its action. In this principle he saw the working of a divine creation for surely this must involve a conscious design and not mere accident.

From a strictly mathematical viewpoint this theory was unfortunate, since it tended to attract to itself a great deal of mystical philosophizing to the detriment and obscurity of the true mathematical principles involved. At the same time it must be admitted that the search for the unifying principle, which was to have useful mathematical by-products, was intensified simply because of its apparent theological significance. Nowadays the principle is accepted over a wide area of application but in a modified form. Nature is now thought to minimize or maximize many of its associated quantities although, as noted above, a minimum value of one quantity often implies a maximum value of some related quantity.

After rhapsodizing over the bees' hexagonal complexes, Pappus also observed that the regular polygon of given perimeter which will enclose the greatest area is the polygon which has the greatest number of angles and that the greatest area of all for the given perimeter is enclosed by a circle. This suggests the area of a circle as the limiting value of the area of regular polygons and is an interesting corollary of Archimedes' thoughts in this direction.

The legendary Queen Dido of Carthage is reputed to have known all about this special property of the circle. When she arrived as a refugee in Africa she asked King Jarbos for a grant of as much land as might be enclosed within the hide of a bull. This seemed a reasonable request and was granted without demur. Dido, however, cunningly had the hide cut into strips and with these she enclosed a circular plot upon which she built her first citadel and named it *Byrsa* from the Greek word for *bull*.

So runs the legend of the founding of fabulous Carthage. It is a pleasing story even though philologists have pointed to the possibility that the name *Byrsa* was a corruption of *Bosra* the Phoenician word for castle. Virgil relates that Dido committed suicide when Aeneas left her. Perhaps she was too clever by half.

Men do not like their women to be too clever; and who knows what conundrums she had posed for him before he made good his escape?

Dido's problem is echoed in the reward of the redoubtable Horatius who was said to have been granted by the Romans as much corn land as two strong oxen could plough round in one day. Macaulay does not say how this was accomplished but it is to be hoped that, constant still in mind, Horatius will have profited from Dido's cunning.

A cunning imagination may also be helpful in providing short-cut solutions to other kinds of problems – notably and appropriately in those requiring the calculation of shortest routes.

In Fig. 33, a camping site on the banks of a river is represented by the rectangle ABCD. AB is part of the river bank. A camper, whose caravan is at point Z in the field, enters the site by a gate at point C. He decides to have a bathe before returning to his caravan. He can bathe anywhere along AB. Where should he bathe so that the total distance walked from C to the river and then on to Z shall be the shortest possible?

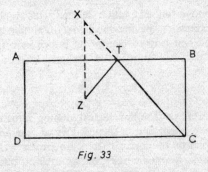

Fig. 33

The simplest way to solve this is to select some landmark such as a tree located at a point X, which is on the other side of the river, so that X and Z are equidistant from AB and so also that the straight line XZ cuts AB at right angles. Point X may in such circumstances be regarded as an image or 'reflection' of Z. The camper should therefore walk directly towards X and he will reach the river bank at T. The total distance represented by CT + TZ is the shortest distance in the conditions specified; for it is equal to CX and this, being a straight line, is the shortest distance between C and X. The distance of any other route would be equal to a distance between C and X other than by the straight line CX and would necessarily be greater.

This example is probably easier to demonstrate theoretically than it is to accomplish in practice. There are many different maximum and minimum problems and mathematics has developed different kinds of methods with which to handle them.

The simplest method of all is based on elementary algebra, but of course this is useful only in connection with relatively simple problems. It has its intriguing aspects nonetheless. The method employs quadratic trinomials of the general form

$$y = x^2 + ax + b$$

having three terms of which one is constant, one involves only the first power of x, and the other involves only the second power of x.

The method is an adaptation of one which employs only binomials (expressions having only two terms) and a study of this basic method will help to clarify the principles involved. The curve of the particular function of this type

$$y = x^2 + 9$$

is shown in Fig. 34. The lowest or minimum value of y on the curve is $y = 9$ when $x = 0$. These values of x and y identify a minimum point on the curve. There is no greatest value because as x increases so also y increases, but again as x decreases below $x = 0$, so y increases. For this particular function the value of y is always positive in sign.

If the function had been $y = x^2$, then this curve would have intersected the y axis at O the origin. The inclusion of a constant value (in this instance the constant is 9) has the effect of moving the whole curve, and so also the lowest point on it, upwards relative to the x axis without having any effect on the shape of the curve itself. The lowest value of y is therefore equal to this constant value as may easily be seen from the equation – when $x = 0$; so $x^2 = 0$; $x^2 + 9 = 9$. There cannot be a lower value than this because x^2 is always positive except only when $x = 0$.

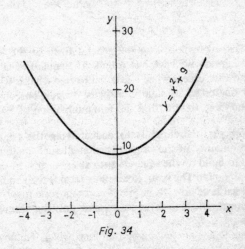

Fig. 34

Accordingly, if we wish to find the lowest value of

$$y = x^2 + b$$

we need only look for the constant value b. If, of course, $b = 0$; then the lowest value of y is also zero. It will make no difference to this conclusion what coefficients appear in the term involving x^2. All terms such as x^2, $2x^2$, $100x^2$ disappear when $x = 0$.

With a little ingenuity a similar principle may be adapted to find the minimum value of a trinomial such as

$$y = x^2 + 6x + 11$$

The curve of this function has a minimum point at which y has its minimum value. If the reader cares to draw the curve of this function he will find that this minimum value is apparently $y = 2$. How may this be proved conclusively by algebra? This is almost ridiculously simple. The first step is to change the form of the function by adding something to it and taking it away again – a common device in mathematics. Thus

$$y = x^2 + 6x + 11 \qquad \qquad \dots\dots \text{ (i)}$$
$$= (x^2 + 6x + 9) + (11 - 9)$$
$$= (x + 3)^2 \qquad\quad + 2$$
$$= z^2 + 2 \text{ (where } z = x + 3)$$

This last expression is in the general form of the binomial whose minimum we have just found. The square of $(x + 3)$ is always positive except when it is equal to zero (that is when $x = -3$) no matter what value is assigned to x. Consequently its minimum value *is* zero, and the minimum value of $y = 0 + 2 = 2$.

The process, therefore, is to deduct from the constant or absolute quantity in the original trinomial such quantity as is required to build up the square – such as $(x + 3)^2$ – in the transformed binomial. The reduced absolute term is then equal to the minimal value of y.

In general, where a is non-zero and positive, the trinomial function

$$y = ax^2 + bx + c$$

may be transformed as follows

$$y = a(x^2 + \frac{b}{a} x) + c$$
$$= a\left[x^2 + 2\left(\frac{b}{2a}\right)x \right] + c$$
$$= a(x^2 + 2dx) + c; \text{ where } d = \frac{b}{2a}$$
$$= a(x^2 + 2dx + d^2) + c - d^2$$
$$= a(x + d)^2 + c - d^2$$

In this final form the original absolute term c has been reduced to $(c - d^2)$. The expression $a(x + d)^2$ vanishes when $x = -d$; and the minimum value of $y = (c - d^2)$. That is, for a minimum y value

$$x = -\frac{b}{2a} \qquad y = c - \left(\frac{b^2}{4a}\right)$$

In equation (i) above, $a = 1$; $b = 6$; $c = 11$. Substituting these values in the results just obtained gives the values $x = -3$; $y = 2$ as before.

When the coefficient a in the trinomial is negative a different set of circumstances arises. The binomial function

$$y = -2x^2 + 8$$

does not have a minimum value because $-2x^2$ is always negative except when it is zero; it cannot be positive. It does, however, have a maximum value. When $x = 0$; $y = 8$ and this is its greatest possible value. The same kind of argument can be developed to identify this maximum value as was used to find the minimum value in the previous example. The process and the numerical results are the same but the difference arises in that when a is negative, the value obtained is a maximum, whereas it is a minimum if a is positive.

The use of this method depends upon our ability to set up equations involving quadratic trinomial expressions. Once this has been done, the rest is simple – as we shall now see.

The number N is to be divided into a sum of two other numbers so that the product of these is the greatest possible. Let one number be x, whence the other will be $(N - x)$. Their product will then be $x(N - x)$ or $(-x^2 + xN)$. The solution therefore requires the maximum value of the function

$$y = -x^2 + Nx + 0$$

The absolute zero term has been inserted to show the general trinomial form. Here $a = -1$; $b = N$; $c = 0$. Substituting these values in the formulae derived above

$$x = -\frac{N}{2(-1)} \qquad y = 0 - \frac{N^2}{4(-1)}$$
$$= \frac{N}{2} \qquad\qquad = \left(\frac{N}{2}\right)^2$$

These show that the maximum product will result from dividing N into two equal parts. If $N = 20$, then the greatest product is $y = 10^2 = 100$. No other pair of numbers summing to 20 can give a greater product. Thus $9 \times 11 = 99$; $8 \times 12 = 96$ and so on.

If we do not restrict our solution to real numbers, as we have done here, we obtain some quite fantastic results, but these must wait until the next chapter.

The same proposition as has just been demonstrated may be rephrased to: 'if the sum of two positive real quantities is given, the product of these is greatest when they are equal'. This again is easy to demonstrate but by quite a different method. Let the two quantities be x and y; their sum $(x + y) = S$; and their product $xy = P$. We first note the identity

$$(x + y)^2 - (x - y)^2 = 4xy$$

So
$$S^2 - (x - y)^2 = 4P$$

and
$$4P + (x - y)^2 = S^2$$

So for any given value of S, the value of P will be greatest when $x - y = 0$; that is when $x = y$.

Since we can find a greatest product within the specified conditions it is interesting and at first surprising to reflect that it is not possible to specify any pair of numbers, summing to a given number N, which will provide a minimum product, although we can make the product as small as we like by taking x, that is, one of the quantities, sufficiently small.

In solving the arithmetical problem of splitting a number into two parts so as to produce a maximum product, we have also incidentally solved the geometric problem of finding the dimensions of a rectangle of maximum area for a given perimeter length. For if the perimeter is of $2N$ units length and one side is x units, then the other side must be $(N - x)$ units. The area of the rectangle is therefore $x(N - x)$ or $(-x^2 + xN)$ square units. We have seen that this expression has a maximum value when $x = N/2$. The rectangle of maximum area for a given perimeter is therefore a square.

This method is now applied to the practical problem of calculating the dimensions of the greatest rectangular beam which can be cut from a section of a tree trunk. It is assumed that this section is cylindrical, and in an actual application it would be necessary to allow for any deviation from this geometric shape after we have established the desired relationships between the optimum dimensions. For any given beam length, the problem is simplified into finding the dimensions of the greatest possible rectangular cross-section area. This is represented by the rectangle ABCD in Fig. 35, the circle representing the cross-section of the trunk. BD is a diameter and is equal to 2R, where R is the radius. Let DC $= x$. Then by Pythagoras' Theorem, BC will be $\sqrt{(4R^2 - x^2)}$ and y, the area of the rectangle, is $x\sqrt{(4R^2 - x^2)}$.

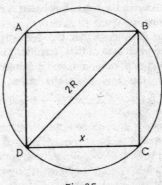

Fig. 35

When y reaches its maximum value so will y^2 reach its maximum. They both reach their maximum values for the same value of x. We therefore find the value of x which will make y^2 a maximum, since this is easier than dealing with the equivalent expression for y.

$$y^2 = x^2 (4R^2 - x^2)$$
$$= -(x^2)^2 + (4R^2)x^2$$
$$= -Z^2 + 4R^2Z; \text{ where } Z = x^2$$

This is in the general form noted above with $a = 1$; $b = 4R^2$; $c = 0$. From the derived formula therefore

$$Z = -\frac{4R^2}{2(-1)} = 2R^2$$

and $x = \sqrt{Z} = R\sqrt{2}$.

In the triangle BCD (Fig. 35) we now have BD $= 2R$; DC $= R\sqrt{2}$. Therefore BC $= \sqrt{(4R^2 - 2R^2)} = R\sqrt{2}$. Thus

$DC = BC$, so that again the rectangle $ABCD$ must be a square to give the maximum cross-section beam area. This example is a practical demonstration of the theorem that of all rectangles which can be inscribed within the same circle, the square which may be so constructed also has the maximum area.

The method of using quadratic trinomials is of limited application. For a more general method we must turn to the differential calculus, but here again the method is based on an idea which is basically quite simple.

It was seen in Chapter 6 that the derivative of a function measures the rate of change of that function. The derivative also has special properties at minimum and maximum points and we can locate these by the symptoms of the former.

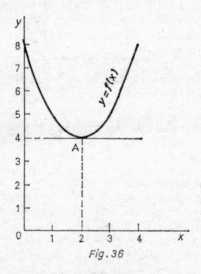

Fig. 36

Fig. 36 shows the curve of the function

$$y = x^2 - 4x + 8$$

It will be seen that the curve falls between the y axis and the ordinate at A but that it then begins to rise. That is, the function decreases up to point A but thereafter increases. It must clearly cease to decrease before it can increase, and the minimum value of the function occurs at the point where this decrease stops immediately prior to the subsequent increase.

At point A the function is neither increasing nor decreasing and its rate of change or the value of its derivative at that point is zero. If therefore we equate the derivative to zero, the solution of the resulting equation will provide the value of x at the minimum point. The derivative of this function and its equating to zero is as follows:

$$\frac{dy}{dx} = 2x - 4 = 0$$

whence
$$x = 2$$

and the value of $y = 4$ can be found by substituting for x in the original equation. This is the value of y at Point A.

The same method, applied to the function

$$y = x^2 + 6x + 11$$

which was previously handled by the trinomial method, produces the result more easily:

$$\frac{dy}{dx} = 2x + 6 = 0$$

$$x = -3$$

whence
$$y = 2$$

The working is straightforward since we knew that we were looking for a minimum value. But the derivative at a maximum point will also be zero. How then can we tell whether the value we obtain is a maximum or a minimum?

Relative to a maximum point the function is increasing immediately before the point and decreasing immediately after the point. But even though it is increasing before the point, the rate of its increase is itself decreasing. That is, the derivative is decreasing just before the maximum point and it continues to decrease right through this point and beyond.

Decrease is mathematically represented as negative increase. The rate of change of the derivative of a function is measured by the second derivative (see Chapter 6) and the sign of this will show how the derivative itself is changing. At the maximum point the derivative is decreasing and so its own rate of change or the second derivative of the original function will be negative.

The converse of this is true for a minimum point where the derivative is increasing and the second derivative is therefore positive.

Accordingly as soon as a point has been identified as either a maximum or minimum point we have the rule that the second derivative

$$\frac{d^2y}{dx^2} \text{ is} \left.\right\} \begin{array}{l} \text{negative for a maximum} \\ \text{positive for a minimum} \end{array}$$

This may be observed in two of the examples already noted. Firstly, the maximum value of

$$y = -x^2 + \mathrm{N}x$$

First derivative: $-2x + \mathrm{N}$

Second derivative: -2 (Negative for a maximum)

Secondly for the function

$$y = x^2 - 4x + 8$$

First derivative: $2x - 4$

Second derivative: 2 (Positive for a minimum)

It should be noted here that not all curves have a maximum or a minimum point even though at some point the derivative may be equal to zero. At such a point on such a curve, however, the second derivative is also zero and this at once tells us that the point is neither a maximum nor a minimum.

On the other hand some functions have both minimum and maximum values and some have more than one of each. An example of such apparently odd behaviour is provided by a curve which undulates across the squared paper and it is evident that the notion of a minimum or maximum value is restricted in some way.

A maximum value of a function is such that the function increases up to that value and decreases immediately afterwards; conversely a minimum value is such that the function decreases before it and increases after it. This functional behaviour is all that is implied in the terms maximum and minimum, and the use of these terms does not mean that the values we calculate are necessarily the greatest or the least of all the possible values of the function.

Maximum and minimum values have a local significance only relative to a specific part of their function's curve. Because of this it is also possible for a minimum point in one part of the curve to represent a value which is greater than that at a maximum point in some other part of the curve.

These restrictions would at first seem to make it difficult to obtain satisfactory solutions to particular problems. If we calculate a maximum value how can we tell if this is only one of a number of maximum values, and if we calculate more than one how can we tell which value we require? In practice, however, these difficulties often do not arise. The conditions imposed in any problem we tackle will normally exercise their own limitations so as to restrict the possible values to a particular range of values.

This then is the way in which differential calculus assists in such problems as have been noted here. Its use in this context is yet another illustration of the facility with which one mathematical process can sometimes be employed in connection with problems which would at first appear to have no point of contact with its main purpose.

The results of maximum and minimum calculations are not always what we might expect to find. What, for example, is the shortest route between two towns on the same line of latitude? At first it seems obvious that the shortest route must be along the line of latitude itself, but this is not so unless the towns are on the equator. The shortest route is along the great circle on which both towns are situated; a great circle being a circle whose centre is at the Earth's centre.

The most surprising results of all are those which await us at the end of the search for the brachistochrone or path of quickest descent. For any two points in the same vertical but not the same horizontal plane, by what path will a sphere roll, without friction and under the effect of gravity only, most quickly from the upper to the lower point?

It is reasonable to assume that the steeper the gradient of a line so also the quicker the journey. Since the straight line between A and B is the shortest distance between those points, then it is also surely reasonable to assume that this straight line will be the path of quickest descent. All very reasonable, indeed, and quite wrong!

It is said in Greek mythology that Sisyphus, a fraudulent King of Corinth is, for his wickedness in this world, forever condemned to roll a marble ball up a hill only to have it roll down again as soon as it reaches the top, with Sisyphus, like Jack or Jill, tumbling after. The Greeks probably thought of his hill as approximating to a straight line of steep gradient, but then they had never heard of the cycloid.

The cycloid is a curve traced out by a fixed point on the circumference of a circle which rolls without slipping along a straight line. This is shown in Fig. 37; AB being the relevant straight line, and C being the fixed point on the circle.

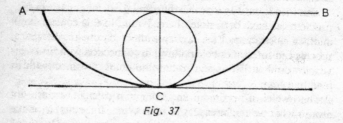

Fig. 37

This is a most remarkable curve. Pascal is said to have staved off a severe attack of toothache merely by thinking about it! It has many mathematically beautiful properties and is sometimes romantically referred to as the Helen of Geometry. Helen, it is true, led to the downfall of Troy while this other Helen too leads to the path of quickest descent. For the astonishing truth is that the sphere will roll most quickly between the upper and the lower point if its path follows the curve of an inverted cycloid. Its progress will then be more rapid than if it had rolled along a plane inclined surface despite the fact that its cycloid path is necessarily longer.

This property was discovered by the Bernoulli brothers but its proof is too involved to be reproduced here. Another remarkable fact is that the final speed achieved by the sphere along the cycloid path is the same as the final speed which would have been attained along the straight line path or any other path! The latter speed would have increased continuously until the sphere reached the lower point; along the cycloid path, however, the speed increases at first much more rapidly but then less rapidly by the time the sphere reaches the lower point.

The cycloid has yet one more astonishing property. It is also the tautochrone – that is to say that a sphere placed anywhere on an inverted cycloid will always take exactly the same period of time to reach the lowest point. The time of descent is quite independent of the height of the starting point!

These properties of the cycloid again remind us that the intuition is a useless guide to mathematical truth. Only a genius could have visualized such properties unaided by adequate mathematical demonstrations – indeed only genius could succeed in identifying these properties at all.

Before leaving the cycloid we may note that although something of a rarity, it was, amongst other mathematical terms, accorded the questionable honour of a mention in *Gulliver's Travels*. Swift, in describing the mathematical shapes into which food had been forced in the palace in Laputa, was satirizing an attitude which he regarded as implying a grossly exaggerated concern for mathematics. Unfortunately he seems to have mixed his ingredients wrongly because he described one of the puddings as being in the shape of a cycloid. The cycloid is a plane figure and not a solid, and the proverbial proof of this particular pudding must certainly have called for a *reductio ultra absurdum*.

10. Imaginary and Complex

The Greeks probably never forgave the natural numbers for pairing off, notably in Pythagoras' theorem, in a not quite respectable manner so as to produce families of irrational offspring possessed of characteristics quite unlike those of the parents. They observed such inexpressible behaviour with distaste.

Their alarm at the sudden appearance of such numbers particularly in a theorem where, had they been expected anywhere at all, they might still have been the least expected, is understandable in the perspective of the restricted Greek view of the number system as a whole. Yet, although they considered irrationals as sufficiently outrageous, even then they did not really know the half of it!

The idea of negative number never occurred to them since it could not have been fitted into their scheme of philosophy. Diophantus, for example, spoke of the 'impossible solution of the absurd equation $4 = 4x + 20$' – impossible because the 'solution' would have been negative. Centuries later Omar Khayyam who, when he was not filling himself with the old familiar juices, was a mathematician of remarkable vision, nevertheless still could not bring himself in spite of his worldly attitude – or perhaps because of it – to admit the possibility of negative numbers.

This supposed impossibility has long since been recognized as an artificial barrier based upon a restricted definition of number in which the concept of negative number had no meaning at all. The eventual recognition of negative numbers as respectable members of the number community was a significant step in the emancipation of mathematics from the dogma of natural philosophy, although this was probably not realized at the time.

The Greeks would have regarded the alleged actuality of negative numbers as bordering on the sacrilegious. What then would they have thought of the laughable pretensions of the square root of minus one? For even after negative numbers had become accepted it was observed that since the square of a negative number, as also of a positive number, was itself always positive, then this effectively precluded the possibility of any square number which was negative. Conversely, therefore, how could a negative number possibly have a square root?

The fallacy in this argument, now disposed of, is rarely if ever exposed in present day writings; yet some comment on it certainly helps to overcome any difficulty which may still arise in attempting a personal resolution of the apparent paradox. The argument would assume that only positive numbers could have square roots because two particular kinds of square roots always produce positive squares. It merely says that positive squares have negative and positive roots and that no negative number can result from the squaring of a root of a positive number. It says nothing about negative squares at all; it takes no account of the possibility of other kinds of square roots.

Such an argument is as illogical as the claim that, since two kinds of brick can be built up into walls, no wall can be broken down into constituent parts which are not these kinds of bricks. But there are many different kinds of brick, and walls may be built in substances, such as concrete and rough stone, which are not bricks at all.

This having been said, however, it is also necessary to say that mathematics, like the building of walls, must conform to certain basic structural requirements. The fact remains that we cannot conceive how 'imaginary' numbers like $\sqrt{-1}$ may be derived from the real numbers (that is, the rational and irrational numbers).

Yet, in this implied expectation that we should be able to do so, we expect too much. The removal of this expectation makes the mind more receptive of the notion of a different kind of number which, while being different, behaves in an arithmetical context just like any other number. It acts like a number and we can resolve the difficulty only if we accept $\sqrt{-1}$ on this pragmatic assumption. Accordingly we define $\sqrt{-1}$ as being a number in its own right such that $\sqrt{-1} \times \sqrt{-1} = -1$. We do not attempt to derive it from any other number.

And so $\sqrt{-1}$ was born; as strange a device to the then contemporary mathematicians as was ever seen amidst the falling shades of night. Yet its birth was not to be legitimized until much later. Cardan, who first used the symbol in 1545, produced it more as an oddity than as a mathematical entity and conceded almost apologetically that such a number was 'useless, imaginary and impossible'.

Euler, who made tremendous contributions to mathematics, also thought that expressions like $\sqrt{-1}$ were 'neither nothing, nor greater than nothing, nor less than nothing, which necessarily makes them imaginary or impossible'. In fact, Euler used imaginary numbers in some of his work and he was apparently the first to use the symbol i for $\sqrt{-1}$. It was not until Gauss adopted them that imaginary numbers finally acquired legitimate status. Nowadays they are of immense importance in vector analysis, relativity, electricity, radio and physics generally. Modern science just could not do without them.

The term 'imaginary' was to remain attached to such numbers as $\sqrt{-1}$, $\sqrt{-2}$ etc. Yet in fact the imaginary numbers proved to have an existence as real, in the literal sense, as any others. The choice of the distinctive labels *real* and *imaginary* was a most unfortunate one and it not unnaturally causes confusion on first acquaintance. This is not really so fundamentally serious as is sometimes asserted. Once a term is mathematically defined then it is the definition, like the smell of Juliet's rose, which is distinctive; the name by which we call it is of little account.

Imaginary numbers eventually force themselves upon the notice of anyone who has much to do with the solving of quadratic equations. They are indeed essential in order that some equations shall have a solution at all. There is a real solution of

$$x^2 - 1 = 0 \text{ (whence } x^2 = 1) \tag{A}$$

but only by admitting imaginary numbers into our system, can there be a solution of

$$x^2 + 1 = 0 \text{ (whence } x^2 = -1) \qquad \textbf{(B)}$$

It would be a sorry commentary upon the vaunted generality of mathematical principles if we could solve some but not all equations of this type. Indeed the admission of imaginary numbers guarantees the existence of solutions to all algebraic equations although this does not necessarily help us towards the actual solutions. Furthermore, with the inclusion of imaginary roots where applicable, it is possible to show that every equation of the nth degree has exactly n roots. Thus is the solution of equations made a more clearly complete operation.

The relationship $x^2 = -1$; or $x = \sqrt{-1}$ arises naturally out of equation B above as a result of elementary algebraic operations once we have accepted the notion of negative number. It is reasonable to assume, with no prejudice to the contrary, that the negative number itself can have roots provided we do not expect them to be the same as roots of positive numbers.

Imaginary numbers open up new fields of mathematical experience and the results obtained are often not what would be expected. Cardan first mentioned them in connection with the problem of finding two numbers whose sum is 10 and whose product is 40. If we restrict our working to real numbers then the problem has no solution. It is not possible to meet the specified conditions.

It was noted in the discussion of maximum values (Chapter 9) that the greatest product of the two aliquot parts of a number is obtained when the parts are equal. The greatest product which can be obtained from the number 10, therefore, is $5 \times 5 = 25$. As this is the greatest possible product it is impossible to obtain the still greater product 40.

Yet this is possible if we introduce imaginary numbers. Thus:

$$10 = (5 + \sqrt{-15}) + (5 - \sqrt{-15})$$

and the product of the two expressions on the right side is

$$5^2 - (\sqrt{-15})^2 = 40$$

The most surprising feature of this example is its generality. We can make the product of the two parts as great as we like merely by selecting the appropriate imaginary number. Expressions such as $(5 + \sqrt{-15})$ which include real and imaginary quantities are called complex numbers.

Cardan regarded his essay into the realm of imaginary number as interesting but meaningless, little knowing that the notion he had reduced to writing would prove to be of immense importance in many physical applications.

We cannot express imaginary numbers in any other form than as the square roots of negative numbers and it might seem that, once we introduce them into equations, they would be likely to persist like unwanted guests to the bitter end. The above example, however, indicates that this is not necessarily true and that the imaginaries often cancel or multiply each other out. The same cannot be said for unwanted guests.

This convenient disappearing trick of imaginary numbers is demonstrated clearly in the following example in which $\sqrt{-1}$ surprisingly helps to establish a relationship between real numbers.

$$(a^2 + b^2)(c^2 + d^2)$$
$$= [(a + b\sqrt{-1})(a - b\sqrt{-1})][(c + d\sqrt{-1})(c - d\sqrt{-1})]$$
$$= (a + b\sqrt{-1})(c + d\sqrt{-1})(a - b\sqrt{-1})(c - d\sqrt{-1})$$
$$= [(ac - bd) + \sqrt{-1}(ad + bc)][(ac - bd) - \sqrt{-1}(ad + bc)]$$
$$= (ac - bd)^2 + (ad + bc)^2$$

This is an interesting relationship between any four given real numbers, the demonstration of which is greatly simplified by the use of $\sqrt{-1}$ which, having done its work as a catalyst, retires gracefully from the final solution.

It was noted earlier that imaginary numbers also make it possible for every equation of the nth degree to have n roots. It follows that every number has n nth roots. Let x be the nth root of the number a. This can be expressed in the equation

$$x^n = a$$
or $$x^n - a = 0$$

and this has n roots – that is n possible values of x which will satisfy the equation. Accordingly the number a has n nth roots. Every number has two square roots, three cube roots and so on. Some of these roots, as was also noted in connection with the roots of equations in Chapter 7, will be imaginary ones.

The cube roots of unity offer an illuminating and simple example of some of the surprising patterns which arise in the land of the imaginary numbers. Let x be the cube root of unity.

Then
$$x^3 = 1$$
and
$$x^3 - 1 = 0$$
so
$$(x - 1)(x^2 + x + 1) = 0$$
whence either $x - 1 = 0$ so $x = 1$ ......(A)

or $(x^2 + x + 1) = 0$ so $x = \dfrac{-1 + \sqrt{-3}}{2}$ ......(B)

or $\dfrac{-1 - \sqrt{-3}}{2}$ ......(C)

The number 1 thus has three cube roots A, B and C. Only A is real; B and C are imaginary. These two imaginary roots have a peculiar relationship. If we square root B, we obtain root C; but also, if we square root C, we obtain root B. These two roots, the Tweedledum and Tweedledee of mathematics, are the squares of each other!

This kind of relationship is unusual in mathematics, but it is not unique, although this particular form is peculiar to imaginary roots. We shall soon come across an example from calculus when we look at a geometrical interpretation of $\sqrt{-1}$.

If we multiply root B by root C we do not, as might be supposed, obtain another complex expression. Instead we find that this product is exactly equal to 1. The real root of 1 is also 1, so that the product of all three roots is again 1.

A more obvious relationship, although still an interesting one, appears in the sum of the three roots. The sum of the two imaginary roots B and C is easily seen to be -1; so that as root A $= 1$, then the sum of all three roots is zero.

Here then are four patterns of great mathematical beauty arising out of the most unpromising material. If we regard B and C as complex numbers in their own right – that is, without for the moment paying any attention to the way in which they were derived above, then

1. the cube of each is 1
2. each is equal to the square of the other
3. their product is 1
4. their sum is −1

The use of imaginary numbers also makes it possible to factorize expressions which do not have real numbers as factors. The expression $a^2 + b^2$ is such an expression; if we admit imaginary numbers it can be 'factorized' as

$$a^2 + b^2 = (a + b \sqrt{-1})(a - b \sqrt{-1})$$

as may easily be checked by multiplying the two factors together.

Some care is necessary in the algebra of $\sqrt{-1}$ and its followers. What is the product of $\sqrt{-a}$ and $\sqrt{-b}$?

Since $$(-a)(-b) = ab$$
So $$(\sqrt{-a})(\sqrt{-b}) = \pm\sqrt{ab}$$

and by reversing this it would seem that the product of $\sqrt{-a}$ and $\sqrt{-b}$ would be positive or negative – that there would in fact be two products. This, however, is not so because

$$(\sqrt{-a})(\sqrt{-b}) = (\sqrt{a} \cdot \sqrt{-1})(\sqrt{b} \cdot \sqrt{-1})$$
$$= \sqrt{ab}\,(\sqrt{-1})^2$$
$$= -\sqrt{ab}$$

This follows logically because the definition of $\sqrt{-1}$ given earlier is in fact restricted to $\sqrt{-1}$ which is positive in sign. It is true that the negative $-\sqrt{-1}$ also occurs but this stems from the definition and is not part of it, just as the negative -1 stems from the definition of the number 1 but is not part of it. The double-product (that is positive and negative) result would only follow if we could derive $\sqrt{-1}$ from 1 instead of defining $\sqrt{-1}$ in its own right.

An amusing fallacy, based on the apparent properties of $\sqrt{-1}$ purports to prove that $+1 = -1$. Thus

$$
\begin{aligned}
1 &= \sqrt{1} \\
&= \sqrt{[(-1)(-1)]} \\
&= (\sqrt{-1})(\sqrt{-1}) \\
&= (\sqrt{-1})^2 \\
&= -1
\end{aligned}
$$

This fallacy arises in the very first step, for while it is true that $1 = \sqrt{1}$, nevertheless, there are really two roots, one positive and one negative. That is, reversing the order of the quantities, the complete relationship is $\sqrt{1} = \pm 1$. One root will lead to one set of calculations; the other root will lead to different calculations. These processes are distinct but the fallacy seeks to combine them. The number 1 results from the squaring of either 1 or -1. If we take the positive root, as in the fallacy, then the correct transformation of $\sqrt{1}$ is $\sqrt{[(1)(1)]}$. The transformation in the fallacy $\sqrt{[(-1)(-1)]}$ results from the negative root. The two separate calculations are

	Positive root	*Negative root*
	$\sqrt{1} = 1$	$\sqrt{1} = -1$
whence	$1 = \sqrt{[(1)(1)]}$	$-1 = \sqrt{[(-1)(-1)]}$
	$= (\sqrt{1})^2$	$= (\sqrt{-1})^2$
	$= 1$	$= -1$

It may be said that imaginary numbers fully achieved respectability as soon as they could be interpreted geometrically, for they thereupon took on a clear meaning in place of the unsatisfactory appearance of a number which yet was not a quantity.

Imaginary numbers may be represented by a system which is based on the ideas of co-ordinate geometry. The latter were devised almost simultaneously by Fermat and Descartes and it is a remarkable coincidence that the extension of their idea was also developed almost simultaneously by two individuals independently of each other. These were a Norwegian surveyor named Wessel and a Parisian book-keeper called Argand.

In the co-ordinate system in Fig. 38, the real numbers are marked off along the x axis. Point A represents the number $x = 1$. Point B represents the number $x = -1$. C is a point on the y axis such that $OC = OA$. Triangle BCA will then be a right

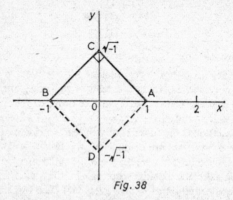

Fig. 38

angled triangle, and OC may be regarded as a perpendicular from C meeting the base at O. OC is therefore the geometrical mean between OB and OA. That is $OB:OC::OC:OA$; or $(OC)^2 = (OB)(OA)$. Therefore

$$OC = \pm\sqrt{[(OB)(OA)]}$$
$$= \pm\sqrt{[(-1)(+1)]}$$
$$= \pm\sqrt{-1}$$

Point C, by its position on the y axis, is positive and we therefore take the positive root, so that point C may be regarded as representing $\sqrt{-1}$ or i. In like manner the point D, placed so that $OC = OD$, will represent the negative root $-\sqrt{-1}$ or $-i$.

By constructing similar triangles relative to other values of x it is possible to site all the other imaginary numbers along the y axis using exactly the same principles.

The successive powers of i are:

$$i = \sqrt{-1}$$
$$i^2 = -1$$
$$i^3 = -\sqrt{-1}$$
$$i^4 = +1$$

and higher powers repeat this periodic pattern. Reference again to Fig. 38 will show that

$$OC = \sqrt{-1}$$
$$OB = -1$$
$$OD = -\sqrt{-1}$$
$$OA = +1$$

These are the same results as are obtained by taking successively high powers of i, so that multiplication by i at each stage represented by these particular line segments may be regarded geometrically as a counter-clockwise operation of rotation through a right angle.

The geometrical representation of Wessel and Argand was itself extended and generalized by Gauss to incorporate all the complex numbers of the form $(x + iy)$ within the plane, every point representing a complex number, and every complex number representing a point fixed by reference to the x and y co-ordinate axes.

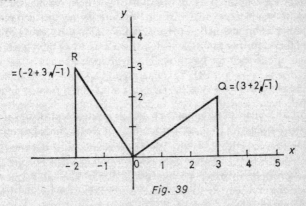

Fig. 39

Fig. 39 shows a co-ordinate system with the real numbers marked off along the x axis and the imaginary numbers marked off along the y axis. The complex number $(3 + 2\sqrt{-1})$ is represented in the plane by point Q. Every other complex number may be represented similarly.

Multiplication of a complex number by *i* may also be represented geometrically as a rotation through a right angle. If the line OQ in Fig. 39 is rotated anti-clockwise through a right angle about O then the point Q would coincide with point R which represents the complex number $(-2 + 3\sqrt{-1})$. This complex number may be obtained algebraically as the product of $\sqrt{-1}$ and $(3 + 2\sqrt{-1})$ the complex number at Q:

$$(3 + 2\sqrt{-1})(\sqrt{-1}) = 3\sqrt{-1} + 2(\sqrt{-1})^2$$
$$= 3\sqrt{-1} + 2(-1)$$
$$= 3\sqrt{-1} - 2$$

The complex number $(3 + 2\sqrt{-1})$, in reference to the co-ordinate axes in Fig. 39, may be interpreted as an instruction to move 3 units along the *x* axis to point P and then 2 units along PQ (which is perpendicular to the *x* axis and parallel to the *y* axis since PQ is the *y* ordinate at P). The point Q is thus uniquely determined.

However, noting *i* as an operator of rotation, we may bring out its significance in this regard by interpeting this complex number as an instruction to move 3 units along the *x* axis to P and then a further 2 units, still along the *x* axis, to Z; subsequently rotating the segment PZ through a right angle about P so as to assume the position PQ. This interpretation shows the complex number $(3 + 2\sqrt{-1})$ as the sum of 3 units and 2 rotated units.

We have seen that $\sqrt{-1}$ operates to rotate a line segment through a right angle about some specified point. This has only a limited application, since successive rotations resulting from this operation effectively identify only four positions of the rotated segment, whereas during its rotation the latter will assume all the possible intermediate positions. What general form of operator is required to permit the identification of all these different positions relative to the different sizes of angle through which rotation is effected?

For this we again have recourse to Pythagoras' theorem and to some trigonometrical manipulations which, although simple in themselves, nevertheless lead to far-reaching results once the operator has been identified.

In Fig. 40 the point P represents the complex number (x + $y \sqrt{-1}$) in relation to x, y rectangular co-ordinate axes. The position of this point may, however, be determined in quite a different way by the use of polar co-ordinates. Thus given a fixed

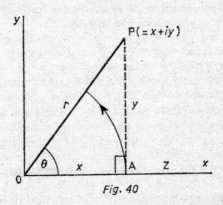

Fig. 40

base or initial line such as OZ, the position of point P may be determined by the size of the angle θ and the length of the line OP, where O is the origin or pole of the co-ordinate system. In this system the line OP is called the radius vector and θ is called the vectorial angle.

If we draw PA perpendicular to OZ then from triangle PAO we may calculate the trigonometrical ratios relative to the angle θ as under, where OP = r.

$$\sin \theta = \frac{y}{r} \qquad \cos \theta = \frac{x}{r}$$

whence $\qquad y = r \sin \theta \qquad x = r \cos \theta$

substituting these equivalents in the complex number $x + y \sqrt{-1}$ transforms it to

$$= r (\cos \theta + \sin \theta \sqrt{-1})\ r \cos \theta + r \sin \theta \sqrt{-1}$$

Just as the complex number in its original form may be interpreted as a movement from O to P, so may this transformed version be interpreted as a movement although this is to be effected in a different way.

The operator $(\cos \theta + \sin \theta \sqrt{-1})$ is interpreted as 'move a unit length along the initial line (to, say, B) and rotate this unit length through the angle θ'. The operator r is interpreted as (following upon the rotation) 'stretch the unit length by r times'. This 'stretch' operator is called a tensor.

The operator $(\cos \theta + \sin \theta \sqrt{-1})$ is the generalized form of the rotation operator of which $\sqrt{-1}$ is a particular form when $\theta = 90°$; since $\sin 90° = 1$; $\cos 90° = 0$.

An example incorporating the above principles will help to make the transformation clearer. Let the complex number $(x + y \sqrt{-1})$ have the particular form $3 + 4 \sqrt{-1}$; whence $x = 3$; $y = 4$; so $r = 5$.

Then also

$$\left.\begin{array}{l} \cos \theta = \tfrac{3}{5} = \cdot 6 \\ \sin \theta = \tfrac{4}{5} = \cdot 8 \end{array}\right\} \text{ so } \theta = 53° \ 8' \text{ (from tables)}$$

Reversing the substitutions

$$\begin{aligned} & r\,(\cos \theta + \sin \theta \sqrt{-1}) \\ = & \ 5\,(\cos 53° \ 8' + \sin 53° \ 8' \ \sqrt{-1}) \\ = & \ 5\,(\cdot 6 \qquad + \cdot 8 \sqrt{-1}) \\ = & \ 3 \qquad\quad + 4\sqrt{-1} \end{aligned}$$

These equivalent forms illustrate a special property of complex numbers. If two complex numbers are equal, that is

$$(a + b \sqrt{-1}) = (c + d \sqrt{-1})$$

then the real parts, a and c, are equal to each other, and the imaginary parts $b \sqrt{-1}$ and $d \sqrt{-1}$, and so, therefore, the quantities b and d are also equal to each other. So in the numbers

$$(3 + 4 \sqrt{-1}) = (5 \cos \theta + 5 \sin \theta \sqrt{-1})$$
$$5 \cos \theta = 3; \qquad \text{so } \cos \theta = \cdot 6$$
$$5 \sin \theta \sqrt{-1} = 4 \sqrt{-1} \text{ so } \sin \theta = \cdot 8$$

This property, taken in conjunction with the results of successive applications of the rotation operator, makes it possible to derive certain trigonometrical equivalents. The operator $(\cos \theta +$ $\sin \theta \sqrt{-1})$ will effect a rotation through an angle of θ. A rotation through a further angle θ will be effected by the further application of this operator. These two successive applications of the operator are together represented as

$$(\cos \theta + \sin \theta \sqrt{-1})^2$$

effecting a total rotation through an angle 2θ.

But the operator for a single rotation through the angle 2θ is

$$(\cos 2\theta + \sin 2\theta \sqrt{-1})$$

from which it will be seen that these two operations are equivalent; that is

$$(\cos \theta + \sin \theta \sqrt{-1})^2 = (\cos 2\theta + \sin 2\theta \sqrt{-1})$$

so $\cos^2\theta - \sin^2\theta + 2 \sin \theta . \cos \theta \sqrt{-1} = \cos 2\theta + \sin 2\theta \sqrt{-1}$

and equating the real parts,

$$\cos^2 \theta - \sin^2 \theta = \cos 2\theta$$

while, equating the imaginary parts,

$$2 \sin \theta . \cos \theta \sqrt{-1} = \sin 2\theta \sqrt{-1}$$
and $\qquad\qquad 2 \sin \theta . \cos \theta = \sin 2\theta$

Here again it will be noted that $\sqrt{-1}$ conveniently drops out of the final results, leaving us with useful expressions of the relationships between the trigonometrical ratios of any angle θ and twice that angle, 2θ.

II. All Set

The part is equal to the whole!

Here is a challenge to the intellect. In what circumstances can this possibly be true? It seems absurd to the intuition that such a claim could ever be substantiated; but intuition is a poor guide in mathematics and is particularly helpless in any attempted visualization of the properties of infinite sets in respect of which the above equality has been asserted.

A set is a collection of things which are called its members or elements. These elements often have a common identifiable attribute but the only essential property common to all elements in a particular set is, in fact, their membership of that set. This membership will itself sometimes imply some other common attribute as a qualification for membership and other attributes may also be inferred from it.

Here we shall be dealing only with sets of numbers, of one kind or another, or of points which represent or may be represented by numbers. A set may be finite, such as the set of the four numbers 1, 3, 5 and 7; or it may be infinite, such as the set of all the natural numbers.

Two sets are numerically equivalent when they each have the same number of elements. The numbers 1, 3, 5 and 7 of a set A and the numbers 2, 6, 10, 14 in a set B are the elements of their respective sets; there are four elements in each set and the sets are equivalent. This is all that the equivalence of sets signifies.

We can count the number of elements in each set separately and then compare the separate totals; or we may satisfy ourselves that two sets are equivalent by showing that every element in one set can be paired off with an element in the other set as was exemplified in the pairing of the fifty sons of Aegyptus with the fifty daughters of Danaus. How such symmetry of related progeny was achieved need not detain us. The essential requirement of this fateful match-making was that there should be just enough husbands – no more and no less – to permit one husband for one wife.

The pairing of the elements of two sets is called one-to-one correspondence. It will be evident that such a correspondence may be established without necessarily indicating how many elements there are in each set. If, however, we establish a one-to-one correspondence between the elements of a set A and the elements, in numerical order, of the set of the natural numbers then we are in effect counting the number of elements in set A.

Set A	1	3	5	7	9
Natural numbers	1	2	3	4	5

The element in this set A can be put in one-to-one correspondence with the first five natural numbers. There are therefore five elements in set A. This process illustrates a suggested definition of counting. Set theory suggests that counting is the process of establishing a one-to-one correspondence between the things to be counted (regarded as the elements of a set) and a sufficient number of consecutive natural numbers in ascending order.

This concept approximates to the intuitive idea. One for the master, one for the maid and one for the little boy who lives down the lane – this counts the bags of wool in much the same way because we know that each of three people has exactly one bag. There is apparently no difficulty about the definition of counting. It may even appear to be so obvious that it does not require mentioning. Yet if we accept this definition with no reservations we must logically accept some astonishing conclusions to which it will inexorably lead us. Whether or not we may in fact be being led up the garden path it certainly takes us into a wilderness which is by no means obvious and is well worth exploring.

Galileo was the first on record as having noted that there is a one-to-one correspondence between the natural numbers and their respective squares.

Natural numbers	1	2	3	4	5	$6 \ldots n$
Squares	1	4	9	16	25	$36 \ldots n^2$

No matter how many natural numbers there are, each one has its respective square. There are as many squares as there are natural numbers. But the numbers in the set of squares also form a subset or part of the set of natural numbers. So there are as many elements in this subset as there are in the whole set.

This is puzzling enough but it becomes even more so when, as Galileo also noted, we observe that the proportionate number of squares diminishes as we take successively higher numbers. In the first hundred natural numbers there are ten squares; that is ten per cent of these numbers are also squares. Only one per cent of all the natural numbers up to 10,000 are squares. The incidence of square numbers contained within the set of natural numbers thus reduces as we proceed to the higher numbers – and yet there are as many square numbers as there are natural numbers.

This paradox puzzled Galileo considerably, and he eventually concluded that it must be invalid to speak of infinite quantities as being greater or less than or equal to each other and that comparisons such as these must be confined to finite quantities. The paradox occurs only in connection with infinite sets.

Whereas Galileo thus dismissed the problem as a paradox it was taken up again some three centuries later by Georg Cantor from quite a different viewpoint. Cantor concluded that the paradox could be resolved only by attributing to infinite sets some specific property not possessed by finite sets, and that the paradox itself provided such a property.

Just as men had had to come to terms with irrationals, negative numbers and imaginary numbers, all of which had at one time seemed equally paradoxical, so apparently the only way to treat the extraordinary behaviour was to accept it. Thus Cantor *defined* an infinite set as one whose elements could be placed in one-to-one correspondence with the elements of one of its own subsets. This assertion is remarkable either for its audacious simplicity or for its enormity according to one's own point of view. Cantor himself confessed that it had cost him a great effort to acknowledge its truth.

Similar ideas in geometry produce equally startling results. In Fig. 41, the line DE is drawn parallel to the base of the triangle

ABC. By construction DE is shorter than CB. How many more
points are there on CB than on DE?

AXZ intersects DE at any point X and also intersects CB at
point Z, the position of the latter being determined by the position
of X. Thus the points X and Z may be paired. X is an element of

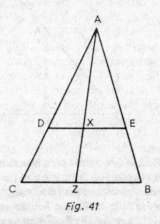

Fig. 41

the set of points on DE; Z is an element of the set of points on
CB. If we draw any other line which intersects both DE and CB
then the points of these two intersections can also be paired. In
general every point on DE can be uniquely paired with its corresponding point on CB, and vice versa. There are therefore as
many points on DE as there are on CB.

This can only occur if the number of points is infinite in each
set. That is, the number of points in each line segment is the same
and, by extension, the number of points in any line segment
irrespective of its length can always be placed in one-to-one
correspondence with the points on any other line segment.

If this seems impossible it is no use rejecting the conclusions
out of hand. Rejection would destroy mathematics. In particular
we would have first to discard co-ordinate systems. In Fig. 42 the
segment OA is part of the curve of some linear function $y = f(x)$
the precise nature of which is unimportant. Each point on the
curve has a pair of co-ordinate (x,y) values relative to the two

axes. Each point is related to one, and only one, point on the x axis for otherwise x would have more than one value at A; similarly each point on the curve is related to one, and only one, point on the y axis.

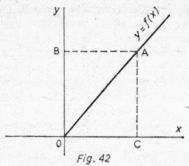

Fig. 42

There is, therefore, a one-to-one correspondence between the elements of the set of points on the curve and the elements of the sets of points on the segments of the respective axes. Yet for any given segment OA on the curve, the lengths of OA, OB and OC are all different! They are all of different lengths yet seem to have exactly the same number of points. Scepticism must at least halt here.

Cantor's ideas are widely accepted today although there are still disbelievers. Whereas Hilbert thought that Cantor had provided a mathematical paradise, his critics claimed that the paradise was merely the plural of paradox. His ideas were subjected to intense ridicule by Kronecker who had once been Cantor's teacher and who was later to ruin his whole career.

Kronecker detested the mere idea of infinity as a number concept. The integers were his religion. 'God made the integers,' he said, 'all else is the work of man,' – a wonder he did not say 'of the devil'. To him those who pursued the infinite were mathematical heretics and a peril to the purity of the whole mathematical structure.

The subject of infinity is one in which ideas tend to slip away as soon as we try to grasp them much as the apples always eluded Tantalus. There is room for doubt. The intriguing aspect of the difficulty of making the intuition accept Cantor's definition is the fact that this difficulty arises out of the ease with which the intuition accepts the notion of counting in relation to one-to-one correspondence. This concept seems beyond dispute, but if we reject the conclusions which inevitably arise out of it must we not also reject the premise that one-to-one correspondence is equivalent to enumeration? Or, like Galileo, must we restrict this concept to finite sets only?

Cantor also declared that there is an infinite number of infinite sets. This leads us straight to another paradox which is often referred to as Russell's antinomy. Does the set of all sets include itself? If this is so, then infinite sets may be classified into two distinct types – those which include themselves and those which do not. Then is the set of all sets which do not include themselves also a member of itself?

This is sometimes translated into simpler terms as the paradox of the barber who shaves all, and none other, who do not shave themselves. Does he shave himself? If he does, he shouldn't; if he doesn't he should! This is not an accurate translation of Russell's antinomy because the set or sets involved are finite. Indeed it is not so much a paradox as a fallacy; it arises direct from the inconsistency in the wording of the barber's activities.

The posing of such problems is as illogical as the requirement that a house be built without doors, coupled with an insistence that entry may be effected only through a door – but who would build such a house except perhaps those philosophers who are weary of ever coming out by the same door wherein they went?

So far as Russell's own paradox is concerned we should perhaps ask whether a set of sets is the same kind of entity as a set of things which are not sets. The paradox may result from a fault in the definition of a set. If a set is to be allowed to refer to any collection whatever then this must include the set of all sets. If, however, a set is defined as a collection of elements which does not include itself as an individual element the paradox would not arise. The barber could be regarded as constituting a separate set by himself; he would not be a member either of those who shaved themselves or of those who did not since he would have to be excluded from these by definition.

Cantor's assertion that, although there are as many square numbers as there are natural numbers, the set of the former is nevertheless a subset of the latter, deserves further scrutiny. Only in this way is it possible to appreciate just what is demanded of the intuition if the theory is to be accepted.

If we take a finite set of consecutive natural numbers and the set of their respective squares, the second set is not a subset of the first.

$$\begin{array}{lcccc} Set\ A & 1 & 2 & 3 & 4 \\ Set\ B & 1 & 4 & 9 & 16 \end{array}$$

Only two of the numbers in set B are also in set A. No matter how large we make the two sets, subject only to the condition that they are finite, the whole of set B will never be included in set A. The forming of successively larger sets is itself an infinite process and it is not easy to accept, therefore, that any set like B can ever be entirely within a set like A if we insist that the two sets always have the same number of elements.

The crux of the matter here seems to be that so long as a one-to-one correspondence is maintained between the respective elements of the two sets, it will never be correct to say that all the elements in set B are also included in set A. And, without the one-to-one correspondence, we no longer have a counting frame at all.

The demonstration that each line segment has the same number of points as any other line segment derives from the nature of those abstractions which we call points. They have no dimensions. How then can they be counted at all so as to justify the statement that there is an equality of numbers?

This is not an empty question. Cantor himself distinguished between infinities which are countable or denumerable and those which are not. A set is denumerable if and only if its elements can be placed in one-to-one correspondence with consecutive natural numbers. The set of points in a line segment apparently cannot be paired with the natural numbers and is not countable. If points cannot be counted is it appropriate to speak of them as being of the 'same number' irrespective of the length of segment?

Thus there are as many square numbers as there are natural

numbers, but of equal sized sets it is never true to say that all the former are included in the latter. Points on one line are said to be of the same number as points on another line, but they cannot be counted. Is there not, perhaps, a suspicion of doubt that, whereas one-to-one correspondence is necessary to the definition of counting, it is not sufficient of itself to validate the extension of this definition to include the counting of infinite sets?

The acceptance of Cantor's theory must also raise doubts as to whether we may properly rely absolutely upon proofs derived from the *reductio ad absurdum* method. His theory depends upon the establishment of one-to-one correspondence between the elements of infinite sets and then proceeds to the paradox that, in some instances, a part of a set is numerically equivalent to the whole set.

Now it pleases us to call this a paradox because it appeals to our sense of incongruity. We accept it only because we can see no alternative. Yet in terms of the *reductio ad absurdum* method such a conclusion would be reduced to an inconsistency which, in the ordinary way, would be taken as disproving the original assumption. It would prove that the elements of infinite sets cannot be placed in one-to-one correspondence.

The difficulty seems to arise in the jump from the establishment of a one-to-one correspondence to the assertion that there are therefore necessarily as many elements in each of the infinite sets between which the correspondence has been established. This again suggests a compromise approach based upon the theory that one-to-one correspondence is necessary and sufficient for counting the elements of finite sets but is not sufficient for counting the elements of infinite sets.

This would destroy the concept of the equivalence between a set and its own sub-set, but it would not destroy those mathematical concepts, such as co-ordinate geometry, which depend upon the one-to-one correspondence between infinite sets but which do not depend upon the counting of the elements of the latter.

How, after all, can we claim to count these elements? Just what is the whole or a part of an infinite set? There is no greatest natural number. We cannot take the sum of all the natural numbers. How then can there be a greatest (that is a total) number of elements in such a set? Galileo may well have been right.

This problem raises issues beyond its own immediate associations. Its roots lie in the mysterious depths of mathematical philosophy among the tangled maze of conflicting fundamentals. We shall return to these later.

Cantor's main concern had been with the concept of number and he used sets as a basis for his theory, but an extremely valuable by-product of his work has been the interest aroused in the concept of the sets themselves.

Set theory has a wide application and many mathematicians believe that it will prove to be a positive factor in the unification of the whole of mathematics. It is true that many other concepts may be translated into the language of sets, and that the theory has remarkable powers of simplification which facilitate the solution of a variety of problems which could not previously have been treated mathematically at all.

This was made possible by the invention by George Boole of a completely new kind of algebra. This, like ordinary algebra, makes for conciseness and simplicity in dealing with problems, but it has a different purpose and admits new kinds of problems to mathematical study. Whereas ordinary algebra deals with relations between numbers, Boolean algebra, of which the algebra of sets is a particular form, provides a bridge between mathematics and symbolic logic and is not restricted to numerical considerations.

Two important operations on sets are union and intersection. The *union* of two sets is the set formed by all the elements in the two sets; if an element appears in both the original sets it will nevertheless appear only once in the union set. In the following sets

$$A \quad 1, \quad 3, \quad 5, \quad 7$$
$$B \quad 5, \quad 7, \quad 9$$

the elements 5 and 7 appear in both set A and set B. The symbol for union is $\cup$, and the union of the two sets shown is

$$A \cup B = 1, \quad 3, \quad 5, \quad 7, \quad 9$$

The *intersection* of two sets is the set formed by the elements common to both sets. The symbol for intersection is ∩, and the intersection of the above two sets is

$$A \cap B = 5, \quad 7$$

Both these operations can be represented in a diagram as in Fig. 43, which is an example of a Venn diagram, so called after J. Venn who originated this kind of diagram.

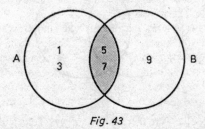

Fig. 43

The two sets are represented by two intersecting circles. The numbers 5 and 7 appear in both sets and are shown in the shaded intersection. In the diagram as a whole each number appears only once; this represents the union of the two sets.

In Fig. 43 the numbers shown are the actual elements of the respective sets. Venn diagrams can also be used to represent the numbers of elements. It is often desirable to deal with the numbers of elements in a set, or in the union or intersection of sets, rather than with the elements themselves. The notation $n(A)$ means the 'number of elements in set A'. In the above sets A and B there are four and three elements respectively; there are five elements in the union set and two elements in the intersection set. So

$$n(A) = 4$$
$$n(B) = 3$$
$$n(A \cup B) = 5$$
$$n(A \cap B) = 2$$

In Fig. 44 is a diagram representing the results of a survey of people who were asked whether they liked tea or coffee or both; each respondent liking at least one of these beverages.

$$70 \text{ liked coffee} = n(A)$$
$$85 \text{ liked tea} = n(B)$$
$$55 \text{ liked both} = n(A \cap B)$$

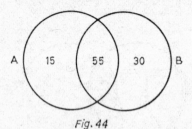

Fig. 44

How many people were there in the survey? To calculate this we need to find the value of $n(A \cup B)$ – the number of elements in the union set. The total number of elements in the two sets is 155.

$$n(A) + n(B) = 155$$

of these, 55 are included twice – once in set A, once in set B.

$$n(A \cap B) = 55$$

The number of different people is given by the union of sets A and B; and this figure is found by deducting (in this instance) 55 from 155 so that the total number of people interviewed was 100. That is

$$n(A \cup B) = 155 - 55$$
or $$n(A \cup B) = n(A) + n(B) - n(A \cap B)$$

This example has been an easy one which could be solved without recourse to special set notation. The same principles can, however, be applied with great success to much more complicated problems.

Fig. 45 shows the intersection of three sets. The union of these sets, that is $n(A \cup B \cup C)$, is identified in much the same way as for two sets. We add together the number of elements in the different sets. This total is $n(A) + n(B) + n(C)$. From this we deduct the number of elements in the intersecting parts of each pair of circles – that is $n(A \cap B)$; $n(B \cap C)$ and $n(C \cap A)$ – since these have all been included twice in the previous total and this deduction is required to remove the duplication.

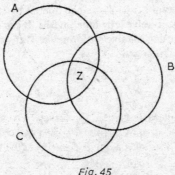

Fig. 45

In doing this, however, we have deducted a little too much. The particular intersection marked Z – that is $n(A \cap B \cap C)$ is included three times in the original total $n(A) + n(B) + n(C)$. Since it is also included in each of $n(A \cap B)$; $n(B \cap C)$ and $n(C \cap A)$ the deduction of these latter items effectively deducts the number Z three times from the original total. Hence Z or $n(A \cap B \cap C)$ must be added back before the union can be completed. Consequently the union of the three sets is:

$$n(A \cup B \cup C) = n(A) + n(B) + n(C) - n(A \cap B) - \\ n(B \cap C) - n(C \cap A) + n(A \cap B \cap C)$$

As an example, let Fig. 45 represent the results of a survey into the readership of three magazines A, B and C. The readers of each magazine form a separate set. There are 100 people in the survey and each one reads at least one of the magazines. Of these:

39 read A	11 read A and B
35 read B	6 read B and C
48 read C	9 read C and A

How many read all three magazines? How many read only A, or B, or C?

This sort of problem seems to have no obvious starting point from which a solution may be attempted and, in order to gain a clearer appreciation of the assistance offered by set theory, it is worth trying first to solve it by other means. It can be solved with the utmost ease using suitable set formulae. Translating the above data into set notation gives:

$$n(A \cup B \cup C) = 100$$
$$n(A) = 39$$
$$n(B) = 35$$
$$n(C) = 48$$
$$n(A \cap B) = 11$$
$$n(B \cap C) = 6$$
$$n(C \cap A) = 9$$

The number of people who read all three magazines is given by the union set $n(A \cap B \cap C)$ which can be obtained from the above formula:

$$100 = 39 + 35 + 48 - 11 - 6 - 9 + n(A \cap B \cap C)$$

whence $\qquad n(A \cap B \cap C) = 4$

Once we have this value we can fill in all the other spaces in the diagram which is repeated in Fig. 46. The original data showed that the intersection of sets A and B – that is $n(A \cap B)$ – included 11 people. This also includes 4 who are also in C. Consequently there are 7 people who are in both A and B, but not in C. This figure 7 can therefore be inserted in the appropriate position in the diagram.

By the same kind of reasoning we can also ascertain the number 5 who are in A and C, but not in B; and the number 2 in

B and C, but not in A. In the intersected parts of A we now have the numbers 4, 5 and 7, totalling 16. Since there are 39 people in A altogether there must be 23 which are in A only. Similarly those only in B are 22; those only in C are 37.

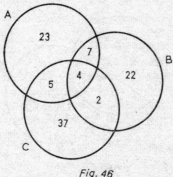

Fig. 46

The following further example illustrates how set theory can substantiate methods for solving problems which may not at first appear to involve the concepts of sets. It is an adaptation of a problem originally proposed by Lewis Carroll. After a battle it is found that of all the casualties exactly 70% have lost an eye; 75% have lost a leg; 80% have lost an arm. What is the least percentage of men to have lost all three?

It is important to note that we are asked to calculate a least possible value; we cannot from the data alone calculate the actual percentage of men who suffered all three injuries.

The simplest way to calculate this least value is to deal not in percentages but in numbers of actual injuries for every 100 men. Between them these 100 men will have suffered a total of 225 (= 70 + 75 + 80) injuries which are 'shared' between them in such a way that as few as possible have all three injuries. This is achieved by assigning at least 2 injuries to each man and a third injury to each of 25 men. Then 75 men have 2 wounds; 25 men have 3 wounds; making a total of 225 wounds altogether. The least percentage to have suffered all three injuries is thus 25%.

It is interesting to translate both the problem and the result into set language and to consider how such a problem can be tackled in that context.

Fig. 47 shows three intersecting sets A, B and C, representing respectively the 70, 75 and 80 men out of each 100 who have

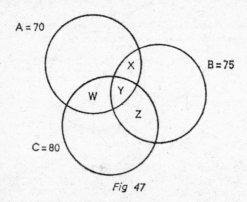

$A = 70$

$B = 75$

$C = 80$

Fig 47

suffered the specified injuries. The intersections are shown by the letters W, X, Y and Z. The section Y represents $n(A \cap B \cap C)$, the value of which we wish to calculate.

Since there are 100 men whose injuries are being considered, then the union of all three sets will contain 100 men. That is

$$n(A \cup B \cup C) = 100$$

also

$$n(A) = 70$$
$$n(B) = 75$$
$$n(C) = 80$$

and from the formula already obtained for $n(A \cup B \cup C)$ we have

$$100 = 70 + 75 + 80 - (X + Y) - (Y + Z) - (W + Y) + Y$$

whence

$$125 = W + Z + X + 2Y \qquad \ldots \ldots \quad (i)$$

If we now take only sets A and B, the total of which is $145 = (70 + 75)$ it is clear that, since there are only 100 men altogether, the least possible intersection $n(A \cap B) = 45$. This is represented in Fig. 47 by the sections X and Y. That is

$$X + Y = 45$$

Similarly by intersecting sets B and C; and then C and A in turn we find that the relevant least possible values are

$$n(A \cap B) = X + Y = 45$$
$$n(B \cap C) = Y + Z = 55$$
$$n(C \cap A) = W + Y = 50$$

so, by adding $X + Z + W + 3Y = 150$

but from (i) $X + Z + W + 2Y = 125$

whence $n(A \cap B \cap C) = Y = 25$

This is the least number of men out of every 100 (equivalent to 25%) to have suffered all three injuries. Also, by substituting for Y in each of the above equations,

$$X = 20$$
$$Z = 30$$
$$W = 25$$

The intersections thus represent 100% of the casualties. This confirms that, for the value of Y to be the least possible, every man must have at least two injuries.

The same result would be achieved in separate stages by first calculating the least possible intersection of two sets; then calculating the intersection between the intersection set so obtained with the third original set, and so on. Carroll's original problem involved four different types of casualty with respective percentages of 70, 75, 80 and 85. If these are taken as sets A, B, C and D respectively, then

$$n(A \cap B) = 70 + 75 - 100 = 45$$
$$n(A \cap B \cap C) = 45 + 80 - 100 = 25$$
$$n(A \cap B \cap C \cap D) = 25 + 85 - 100 = 10$$

So the least possible solution to Carroll's problem is 10%. That is, 90 men have 3 injuries and the other 10 men have 4 injuries. This totals 310 and agrees with the sum 70 + 75 + 80 + 85.

The result illustrates two interesting points. One is the important fact that

$$n(A \cap B) \cap C = n(A \cap B \cap C)$$

The second point is that the general solution of this type of problem, where there are n intersecting sets of percentages, is obtained by adding the percentage numbers and then deducting $100 (n - 1)$. The solution to Carroll's problem, where $n = 4$, is

$$70 + 75 + 80 + 85 - 100 (4 - 1) = 10$$

The solution to the previous problem, where $n = 3$, is

$$70 + 75 + 80 - 100 (3 - 1) = 25$$

This may appear to lead to a paradox in some cases. If, for example, there are six sets representing 90, 70, 60, 50, 40, 75 per cent respectively, then the sum of these numbers (= 385) less 100 $(6 - 1)$ or 500 gives the result -115. The least possible percentage of elements in all six sets thus appears to be a negative quantity. In effect, however, this means that the least possible percentage is in fact zero. That is, the elements of the union set of all the original six sets can be so distributed that there need not be any element which is common to all the sets.

These few examples must suffice, within our limited scope, to provide an indication of some of the basic ideas of set theory and Boolean algebra. It would be wrong, however, to leave the impression that these processes are restricted to the types of problem shown here. Boolean algebra, for instance, has made possible the development of symbolic logic, has facilitated the design of electrical circuitry and, by virtue of its participation in these areas of activity, has made important contributions to the design of computers.

From the purely theoretical standpoint, the theory and language of sets are of immense significance in providing a universal or, at least an almost universal basis for mathematics. This fundamental significance however, which together with the intricate patterns it reveals is of such intense interest to the enthusiastic mathematician, unfortunately tends to make a detailed study of the subject of rather less appeal to the ordinary reader. It is all so basic that to the uncritical many of its assertions seem to be repetitively self-evident and unnecessary. Yet its basic qualities provide its intrinsic value; they are indeed so fundamental that we often employ the notion of sets without realizing that we are doing so.

An inkling of this may be obtained from one or two very simple examples. First we may see how lowest common multiples and highest common factors may be featured in a set context. The prime divisors of a number may clearly be regarded as the elements of a set since, subject to one provision, they are distinguishable from each other and also from all other numbers not contained within their set.

Set A	prime divisors of 30:	$\{1, 2, 3, 5\}$
Set B	prime divisors of 70:	$\{1, 2, 5, 7\}$

The intersection of these sets; that is

$$A \cap B = \{1, 2, 5\}$$

contains the common prime divisors of the two numbers, so that their product is the highest common factor (or greatest common divisor) of those numbers. That is, H.C.F. = 10.

The union of sets A and B; that is

$$A \cup B = \{1, 2, 3, 5, 7\}$$

and the product of the elements in this set is the lowest common multiple of the two original numbers. That is L.C.M. = 210.

In the factorization of some numbers a particular prime or primes will appear more than once. The number 40 has the prime divisors 1, 2, 2, 2, 5. For the purpose of set operations each of these divisors must be treated as a separate element in the set of divisors and, to avoid confusion, it is usual to distinguish them by the use of suffixes or subscripts. The set of prime divisors of this number would thus be shown as

$$\{1, 2_a, 2_b, 2_c, 5\}$$

Divisors more or less form themselves off into sets. Another example, taken from co-ordinate geometry, shows a basic set principle which is rather more hidden. The solution of the two simultaneous linear equations A and B.

$$\left.\begin{array}{ll} \text{A:} & 2x - y = -1 \\ \text{B:} & 3x - y = 1 \end{array}\right\}$$

may be represented graphically by drawing the curves of the two functions of x implicit in the equations

$$\begin{array}{ll} \text{A:} & y = 2x + 1 \\ \text{B:} & y = 3x - 1 \end{array}$$

Each point on the curve of a function is represented by an ordered pair of (x,y) values and each of these pairs can be regarded as an element of the set of all such pairs.

Here we have two curves each representing different functions of x and therefore also representing different sets of ordered pairs of (x,y) values. These may be referred to as Set A and Set B to relate each to the equation with the same distinctive letter. The two curves intersect at just one point, and this point also therefore represents the intersection of the two sets represented by the curves. This point thus represents $A \cap B$, the intersection set, and this contains only one ordered pair $(2,5)$. This, then, is the only ordered pair common to both sets and it provides the solution to the simultaneous equation $x = 2$; $y = 5$.

12. Euclid Unparalleled

For some two thousand years Euclid was the personification of geometry, and no one during all that time seems to have seriously considered that this might ever be otherwise.

This is not to say that all his work was accepted without question. Many of his successors over the centuries were to point to certain weaknesses of presentation and to express dissatisfaction with some logical aspects within the structure of his geometry itself. None of them before 1800, however, entertained the slightest doubt that Euclid *was* Geometry or suspected that other kinds of geometry besides Euclid's were even conceivable.

It was not until Lobachewsky scandalized his contemporaries at Kazan University in Russia in the nineteenth century with his apparently outrageous assumption – to which we shall refer later – that this possibility of other geometries was first presented to a singularly unimpressed public. Since then the whole concept of geometry has undergone a radical change. Euclid's geometry is now recognized as a particular case of a generalized or absolute geometrical structure.

Whether or not this development may be regarded as detracting from Euclid's reputation as supreme arbiter depends upon many considerations. This question cannot be satisfactorily attempted without some reference, however incomplete, to the origins of geometry and the ideas which have from time to time been accepted as to its true nature and purpose.

According to the Greek tradition, geometry originated in Egypt as a collection of rules for the measurement and marking out of land areas. Herodotus, for example, throws an intriguing light upon the practical emphasis in the relation between geometry and the age-old problem of tax assessment. Revenue was raised by the taxation of land, and complications regularly arose because of the devastations caused by the marauding waters of the flooding Nile. Official surveyors, no doubt watchful for the prevalent forms of tax evasion, were then called in to measure the altered areas of individual plots.

Herodotus solemnly assures us that this 'was the origin of Geometry', adding laconically, 'which then passed into Greece'. This account, although less fanciful and entertaining than many of his other stories, nevertheless shares with them the evidence that Herodotus suffered from the twin disability of not being able to resist a good tale – which is harmless – and of being apt to jump to conclusions – which is not so harmless. It probably underrates the achievements of the Egyptians, not to mention the Babylonians and Sumerians before them, in that the solution of their tax problem was probably achieved by the application of pre-existing rules and did not, as Herodotus suggested without much justification, itself give birth to the rules.

His account certainly overrates the value of the supposed Egyptian origins of geometry as a science, at the expense of the tremendous Greek contribution. Although the Egyptians and the Babylonians had a limited number of practical mensuration rules of varying degrees of accuracy, there is no evidence to suggest that they had general proofs of these rules or that they had any idea of geometry as a pure deductive science. It is probably more correct to say that their rules revealed some of the possibilities and indicated the desirability of the development of a formal geometry.

The full flowering of the elegantly aesthetic geometry, as it was eventually to be recorded by Euclid, is almost entirely attributable to the ingenuity and tireless search for truth by the Greek philosophers. Many made their personal contributions to this but Thales (about 600 B.C.), one of the Seven Wise Men of Greece, is generally regarded as the man who brought the Egyptian rules to Greece and fashioned from them the basis of a geometrical science.

To him falls the honour of having first realized that there was any advantage, practical or aesthetic, to be derived from a consideration of the many interrelated properties of geometrical figures as distinct from the mere utility of a few rules which employed some of those properties. Today, when many of the basic ideas of Euclidean geometry are taken more or less for granted, it is not easy to appreciate just how remarkable an insight must have been required to contemplate such a momentous step.

The practical rules of the Egyptians were relatively simple and limited in application to small areas. The Greeks were to widen the scope of geometry so as to admit theoretical deductions which, although they might have incidental practical applications, were essentially regarded as of interest in themselves. Some of the limitations implicit in the practical rules were, however, unwittingly carried through into the theoretical structure. This resulted, not so much from any weakness in the theory, as from the then current views on the nature of geometry.

The word 'geometry' originated from two Greek words meaning 'earth measurement'. The use of such a name clearly shows the origins from which the subject sprang and although, even in Greek times, it had come to be divorced from mere land measurement, it was nevertheless still regarded as being concerned with physical reality. Its revelations were accepted as absolute truths of man's very existence. Yet paradoxically, as we shall note later, the propositions of Greek geometry, while apparently satisfactory for relatively small land areas, are nevertheless not suitable for dealing with larger areas of the earth's surface.

So great was the Greek influence in geometrical matters that Euclid's *Elements* came to have an authority not much less than that of the revered books of religion. It is not surprising that this should have been so in Greek times since mathematical knowledge – the properties of number and the supposed absolute truths of geometry – traditionally formed part of their mystical beliefs as divine manifestations. Although, by Euclid's day, geometry was no longer merely a science of the ideal, the apparent inevitability of its conclusions was still unquestionably accepted.

That this influence should have continued so strongly to comparatively modern times is much more surprising. This is probably due mainly to the work of Euclid, for even when the mystique had been removed from Greek geometry there still remained the solid achievements of his *Elements*. This was an impressive and monumental codification of geometric principles, which had been established by his fellow Greeks and others, into one apparently consistent structure of theory, the beauty and self-sufficiency of which permitted no serious rivalry.

Euclid was something of a phenomenon even in his own day. Other writers before him had compiled similar works but, such was his impact, that these were all superseded. Euclid made no claim to originality. His peculiar genius rested in an ability to present the work of others in a coherent, logical and generally satisfactory scientific manner as judged by the standards then current.

That there are imperfections in his work, when viewed through the more modern microscope of mathematical logic, cannot be disputed, but in the two thousand and more years since the *Elements* was published in about 300 B.C., Euclid has suffered more than his fair share of editing. His approach to the very basis of geometry has often been interpreted differently, and this point is of some importance in what follows here.

Euclid arranged his propositions and theorems, insofar as it was possible, so that each result followed logically upon previous ones. Not all results may be so happily founded, however. The simplest form of logical system consists of certain premises and the drawing of conclusions from them. Each conclusion so reached may itself then be regarded as a new proposition and, perhaps, as a premise leading to still further conclusions. The whole of mathematical theory is built up in this way, and the ingenuity of man in finding which propositions can be linked together provides the stepping stones to mathematical discovery.

A proposition, which originates as the conclusion from a series of other propositions, carries with it an apparently respectable assurance of pedigree. When we try to trace this pedigree to its origins, however, we encounter a difficulty which is almost as embarrassing as that of the man who is said to have paid a small fortune to have his family tree traced and twice as much to have it hushed up.

Logic reasons from some assertion of fact, and the logical structure built upon that assertion clearly cannot be used to prove the truth of the assertion itself. This may seem a trite comment, but its implications are tremendous. It forces upon us the distasteful realization that, unless we accept some self-evident 'truths' as our basis for reasoning, we cannot construct a logical system to reveal other truths at all.

That there are such original truths, upon which a system may be constructed, need not be doubted, but we must face the plain fact that we cannot legitimize them by our reasoning alone. Something which appears to be self-evident may not in fact be true. This means that, for all our insistence upon deductive method, this can in the final analysis, however remote, be seen to be based precariously perhaps upon an original process of induction.

Propositions which are self-evident to some observers may possibly not be self-evident to others. Proclus relates, for example, that the Epicureans ridiculed the theorem that the sum of the lengths of two sides of a triangle is greater than the length of the third side. This was not because the theorem was incorrect, but because it was so evident 'even to an ass' as not to require any proof at all.

The possibility of dangers arising from the intrusion of our intuition and the induction method was fully apprehended by the Greeks. They realized that the number of assumed truths must be kept to an absolute minimum; for not only was there the danger that these might prove to be false, but regard must also be taken of the fact that many of the truths of mathematics could never be known from induction or experience alone. Pythagoras's tragic discovery of incommensurables could never have been suggested by intuition alone.

Euclid built his geometry upon a number of assertions which he variously called 'common notions' and 'postulates'. These terms have been taken by some translators to be roughly interchangeable but it is important, in considering Euclid's approach to his subject, to study whether this really was his intention. It seems reasonable in fact to suppose that he did not regard his notions and postulates as being of precisely the same character. Had he done so, he need have used only one term, instead of two, to describe them.

He appears instead to have thought of his common notions as

truths which were so self-evident as to require no demonstration, whereas his postulates appear to have been propositions (rather than assumed truths) which, while not being self-evident, were nevertheless eminently reasonable but could not be established by proof based only on the common notions. This grouping of ideas had already been suggested by Aristotle, common notions being assumptions common to all sciences and postulates being assumptions specifically relevant to a particular science.

This distinction has often been disregarded, and many editors have grouped the notions and postulates together (and added some of their own) into one system of axioms. This undoubtedly served their own immediate purposes of presentation in teaching geometry and in stating explicitly some further notions which Euclid tacitly assumed. Euclid's own grouping is of paramount importance when considering the development of geometry.

Euclid enumerated five common notions and five postulates. The notions deal entirely with equalities and inequalities (for example, 'things which are equal to the same thing are equal to one another'); whereas the postulates refer more to the possibility of specified geometric constructions. The first four postulates are: a straight line may be drawn from one point to any other point; a terminated straight line may be produced to any length in a straight line; a circle may be described from any centre at any distance from that centre; all right angles are equal to one another.

The fifth postulate is the famous – or infamous – parallel postulate which was to give headaches to so many mathematicians and was eventually to lead to a reappraisal of the nature not only of geometry but also of the whole of mathematics. This postulate is given in various forms in different editions of the *Elements* but is essentially as follows. If a straight line meets two straight lines so as to make the two interior angles on the same side of it taken together less than two right angles, these straight lines being continually produced shall at length meet on that side on which are the two angles referred to.

This postulate has an involved wording, and other mathematicians have attempted both to simplify it and also to re-state it in a form more consistent with a self-evident notion rather than as a postulate. Playfair's axiom, for example, asserts that two intersecting straight lines cannot both be parallel to the same straight line; and this is also equivalent to the assertion that through any given point there is at most one line which can be drawn parallel to a given straight line.

While most of the postulates and notions have usually been accepted without much demur, the fifth postulate was probably always the subject of controversy, although the nature of this controversy was to take a startling change of direction with the advent of Lobachewsky.

Euclid has been reproached by many commentators because the postulate is not self-evident and it is indeed true that, since it implies the possibility of drawing lines of infinite length which are outside our human experience, it can scarcely be self-evident. The same doubt must surround the second postulate for the same kind of reason, and Playfair's axiom, which is much simpler and elegant than Euclid's postulate, tends by its apparent simplicity to cloak the fact that it still involves the concept of a line of infinite length.

Self-evidence in respect of physical phenomena must be restricted to our field of experience, and it is a paradox that equidistant parallel lines of any appreciable length, as on an athletics track, appear to approach each other when viewed from a distance. This, however, is an optical illusion. By ourselves proceeding in the direction of the lines we can see that, fortunately for the athletes, the lines do not intersect.

It is also paradoxical that while the 'truth' of the postulate was never doubted, Euclid's alleged claim of its self-evidence *was* doubted; yet Euclid probably made no such claim. To reproach him for this supposed belief is really to misunderstand the distinction between his notions and postulates, and the outcome of all the controversy was in fact to have a vital bearing on the 'truth' of the postulate, not on its self-evidence.

Whether or not criticism was misplaced, the dissatisfaction with the postulate was nevertheless fully justified. It is perhaps noteworthy that Euclid deferred its use in the *Elements* for as long as he possibly could. If it was not self-evident, how could it be relied upon to give valid conclusions? It certainly was not self-evident and many attempts were made to prove it as a theorem. This followed naturally from the general belief that the assumption was correct. The critics were concerned primarily with the affront to geometrical propriety by the inclusion of a non-obvious and unproved assumption.

Euclid's own wariness suggests that he may have tried to prove the postulate but had been forced to include it as an unproved assumption. The possibility of such a proof being discoverable was kept tantalizingly alive but, despite all the ingenuity and tenacity of purpose which was lavished upon it by a great number of very perplexed gentlemen, every attempt to prove the postulate as a theorem based on the other postulates and notions resulted in dismal failure. So they lost their tempers and started to call it rude names. Already in the fifth century A.D., Proclus had dismissed it as a merely plausible and unreasoned statement. Henry Savile, perhaps more in sorrow than in anger, referred to it as one of the two great blemishes in the beautiful body of geometry, while D'Alembert bluntly called it the scandal of geometry.

Gradually it dawned upon the investigators that perhaps the reason for their failure to find a proof was simply that no proof was possible. This was finally established in a demonstration which, once certain remarkable new propositions had been digested, was elegantly simple.

In the 1820s the mathematical world had been presented with the apparently heretical observations of the Russian mathematician Nikolai Lobachewsky who questioned the 'truth' itself. If the postulate was not necessarily true it could at best be a supposition. This would imply that Euclid's postulate should be prefixed by the conditional 'Let it be supposed that...'

Let us suppose nothing of the sort, retorted Lobachewsky; let us assume instead that at least two parallel lines can be drawn. To his astonishment he found that he could construct an entirely new and logically self-consistent structure of propositions by taking this assumption as a postulate together with Euclid's other four postulates. Nowhere did this lead to any contradictions. Yet is was not merely *not* self-evident; it was also patently absurd to most of those few contemporaries who even bothered to consider it. Lobachewsky at first called his structure an imaginary geometry but later, when he had presumably realized more of its implications, he renamed it Pangeometry.

At much about the same period a very similar idea had occurred to the Hungarian Janos Bolyai. The possible negation of Euclid's fifth postulate had led him also towards the concept of an absolute geometry, of which Euclid's would be a particular case. In 1823 he wrote to his father: 'I have made such wonderful discoveries that I am myself lost in astonishment...out of nothing I have created a new and wonderful world.'

The geometry of Lobachewsky and Bolyai may best be presented by reference to a diagram. In Fig. 48, AB is a straight line.

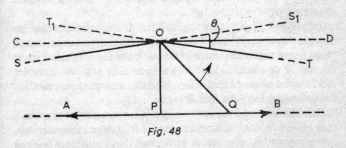

Fig. 48

O is a point not on AB. OP is the perpendicular from O on AB. Q is any point on AB. As Q moves along AB away from P in the direction of the arrow, the distance PQ tends to infinity. At the same time, the line OQ rotates about O and tends to the limiting position OT. OT is said to be parallel to PB.

In the same way, as Q moves along AB in the opposite direction, the line OQ will tend to another limiting position OS. OS is said to be parallel to PA. But PA and PB are segments of AB; consequently both OT and OS are parallel to AB.

According to Euclid's assumption, the lines OT and OS would together form one continuous straight line coinciding with the line CD. According to Lobachewsky's assumption OT and OS are distinct and separate lines. This is based on the assumption that the process of moving Q may be carried on indefinitely. No matter how far we take Q it is always on line AB. Lines OT and OS continuously approach line AB but do not intersect it.

If we extend SO to form the line SOS_1; and TO to form the line TOT_1, then since neither OS nor OT intersect AB, so none of the infinite number of lines through O drawn between the lines SOS_1, and TOT_1, will intersect AB. That is, all lines falling within this angle will fail to intersect AB.

This may seem ridiculous from a glance at the diagram. We are concerned, however, with a process of logic and not with the interpretation of principles from a diagram which is given merely to describe the nature of Lobachewsky's postulate. It is difficult, if not impossible to represent non-Euclidean geometry satisfactorily by way of figures drawn in a flat plane since such figures have inevitably become identified with Euclidean concepts.

The line OT, if sufficiently produced, might reasonably be thought to intersect AB. This is an expectation without logical basis, being merely the result of the conditioning of mind which is the legacy of Euclid. How do we *know* that OT will intersect AB? Euclid assumed that it would unless it formed part of CD; Lobachewsky assumed that it would not.

A doubt, based on the popular idea of the meaning of 'parallel', may arise whether the line OT, even if it does not intersect AB, is necessarily 'parallel' to it. It is clear that these lines are not equidistant in the same way as we have come to expect of the parallel lines encountered in Euclid's geometry. They do not behave at all like Euclid's parallels which remain equidistant throughout. The distance between Lobachewsky's parallel lines diminishes in one direction along the lines and increases without limit in the other directions. Lobachewsky's parallel lines are asymptotes.

Euclid, however, did not define parallel lines as being equidistant. Men came to regard them as such because of the results following from his fifth postulate. Euclid defined parallel lines as those which do not intersect no matter how far they may be produced. Had he defined them as straight lines which are equidistant throughout, then his postulate would have followed as a theorem instead of an assumption, but he would still have been assuming that equidistant lines could exist.

It is a matter for conjecture whether Euclid really thought of parallel lines as being equidistant. In view of the wording of the fifth postulate and the results derived from it, it appears that he did. If this is so, then his definition was not suitable. Indeed, most of his definitions have called forth criticism at one time or another. His list of definitions is more like the list of a play's *dramatis personae* in which he makes a short note against each name so as to assist recognition. We cannot judge the characters in a play merely from these notes. We must instead see the play. The full significance of geometrical concepts may only be gained from geometry itself. Its basic terms cannot be defined in the fullest sense. It is remarkable how easily the mind can grasp such abstractions with such meagre assistance from their descriptions.

Even so, some of Euclid's definitions are certainly oddly worded. Although he supposedly defines many concepts by their positive properties, he attempts to define some by saying, not what they are, but what they are not. A point is that which has no magnitude. This does not suggest what a point actually is. On the other hand, as Gauss was to point out, the definition of a plane 'which wholly contains the line joining any two points' contains more than is necessary to the determination of the surface and tacitly involves a theorem which requires proof.

Nevertheless it is amusing to ponder awhile and to speculate whether, if Euclid had included the property of equidistance in his definition of parallel lines and had developed his postulate as a theorem, the non-Euclidean geometries would ever have seen the light of day.

Lobachewsky and Bolyai seem to have arrived at their surprising conclusions quite independently of each other. Each is entitled to honourable mention. It would be tedious, however, to repeat both names every time, and it might be too facetious to refer to both by some composite word in the way that Bernard Shaw referred to G. K. Chesterton and Hilaire Belloc collectively as The Chesterbelloc in the professed disbelief that there could be two people with such identically unconventional opinions. Instead, we shall refer here to Lobachewsky alone, it being understood that, for the most part, this should also be taken as a reference to Bolyai. Bolyai was advised by his father to publish his conclusions without delay, but Lobachewsky published his first and cornered this particular market.

Gauss the 'Prince of Mathematics', who made immense contributions to many branches of mathematics, was also very exercised over the problems of parallelism. He seems to have reached much the same conclusions, even before Lobachewsky, but to have refrained from publishing them because he feared the outcry which might be expected to follow such heretical imaginings. The word 'non-Euclidean' to describe the new geometries seems to have been invented by him – it appears in a letter of his dated 1824.

Other men too had come close to the discovery of these other geometries but had apparently retreated from the awful prospect. As early as 1733 – almost a century previously – the Italian Saccheri had originated the method of approach which Lobachewsky subsequently followed. But whereas the latter had assumed his alternative postulate in a spirit of adventure to see where it would lead, Saccheri had made a similar assumption with the declared intention of proving it false. He came to praise Euclid, not to bury him.

Saccheri failed in his objective. He could find no inconsistencies in the propositions which followed the alternative assumption, but these propositions themselves seemed absurd enough to be refuted. They were indeed so weird when judged from the Euclidean standpoint that he retreated from them in horror, discarding the discovery of his intellect in face of the stubbornness of his intuition.

Since the postulates of Euclid and Lobachewsky are quite different, they naturally lead to different conclusions. In Euclidean geometry the sum of the three interior angles of any triangle is invariably 180°. In Lobachewsky's geometry we have the bewildering theorem that this sum is less than 180° and that the amount by which it falls short of 180° is proportional to the size of the triangle. The smaller the triangle so the more closely does the sum of the angles approximate to 180°.

Some theorems are identical in both geometries as, for example, the theorem that the sum of the length of two sides of a triangle is always greater than the length of the third side. On the other hand, the most significant difference is that, whereas the theorem of Pythagoras is central to Euclidean geometry, this theorem does not hold in Lobachewsky's geometry.

Well might Saccheri have been horrified and well might some sympathy still be reserved for those who, reared on the Euclidean gospel, find it difficult to reorientate their geometrical beliefs.

Many questions inevitably arise. Is the structure of Lobachewsky strictly a geometry in exactly the same sense as is Euclid's? How *can* there be different geometries? Does not Lobachewsky's imaginary geometry contradict a bastion of Euclidean belief? How can they both be right? Was Euclid, then, wrong? Are the geometries alternative or does acceptance of one exclude the other? Which is the true geometry? Which, if either, properly relates to the physical world?

Some of these questions are really irrevelant. They arise from a misconception of the true nature of geometry. They also derive from a confusion between pure mathematical principles and the application of those principles – a confusion which was adopted into the concept of geometry from the very beginning.

Euclid's geometry had always been accepted as descriptive of the physical world, being based on assumptions which, except for the parallel postulate, appeared to be entirely consistent with what men knew of reality. The parallel postulate itself, although seemingly requiring proof, was not an assumption with which reasonable people could readily disagree. The conclusions, too, of Euclidean geometry did not appear in any way to be inconsistent with reality. The whole elegant system had been developed with acceptable logic and was obviously so aesthetically satisfying that all the evidence seemed to point to the essential rightness of this one and only geometry.

But logic can proceed to valid conclusions only if the preliminary assumptions are correct. Accordingly Euclidean geometry is true of reality only so far as its original assumptions are also true. If these assumptions are true, however, in the absolute sense relative to some physical application, then any assumptions which contradict them cannot also be true. What reason have we for accepting Euclid's postulate rather than Lobachewsky's? We have no reason at all, in the general theoretical sense, although this is not necessarily true in relation to application of the various theories. Furthermore, now that the supposed uniqueness of Euclid's geometry has been destroyed, we must allow for the possibility of still other kinds of geometries – and we shall shortly find this to be a real possibility.

Any one or perhaps none of these may describe reality just as it may or may not have other applications, but the use of geometry in relation to reality must be treated strictly as an application of theory and not as the *raison d'être* of geometry itself. It is no longer of vital interest to any geometry how lines behave or misbehave themselves in outer space. This is a matter for the physicists. Geometry is a logical process of drawing particular conclusions from particular suppositions although it is, of course, more specifically angled towards dimension than to number.

Gone forever is the myth that geometry can tell us anything definite about the physical world. It can, of course, describe certain physical phenomena with sufficient apparent precision so as to suggest that in these particular instances it also demonstrates their absolute truths. The sad fact remains, however, that this apparent facility is no proof of its own validity. Bertrand Russell expressed this in the declaration that geometry throws no more light upon the nature of space than arithmetic throws upon the size of the population of the United States.

It is interesting to note, in passing, that Euclid does not make use in the *Elements* of the infinite-length property of straight lines. He does not seem to have concerned himself with what happens to lines when they depart from the field of human experience. He extends his lines only so far as is necessary to demonstrate his propositions and he seems to have been more concerned with this property of extensibility.

There is also an intriguing combination of paradoxes to be observed. Dissatisfaction with Euclid's fifth postulate was always expressed in terms of our inability to postulate with certainty what happens in the realms of physical space beyond our experience. This implied that geometry was essentially an applied science, whereas it is now shown to be entirely abstract. There was thus no logical reason for this particular form of dissatisfaction. Those who sought to reconcile geometry with reality little realized that their efforts would end in divorce. Euclid always treated geometry as abstract. His reputation, which might have been expected to have been tarnished by its exposure to the airing of controversy, instead emerges shining as brightly as ever.

The divorce of abstract and physical considerations and the consequent dissipation of the mists of confusion made it possible to concentrate more closely on the structure of pure geometry. Different geometries based on different postulates can and do exist side by side. The only basic difference between Euclid's and Lobachewsky's geometries is in one of the initial assumptions. All the other assumptions are identical and each system is logically self-consistent although, as previously noted, they have many conflicting features one with the other.

This disposes of the question as to whether Euclid's fifth postulate can be proved, for if this were possible then Lobachewsky's geometry based on a contradictory postulate would not also be self-consistent.

Each system is equally entitled to be described as geometry, just as computer programmes are all entitled to be called computer programmes even though they are different from each other. There is no valid question as to which is the right geometry or the right computer programme as such, although it is valid to ask which geometry or which programme is best suited to a particular application. This is more evident in respect of computer programmes since these are specifically designed for actual applications.

It is equally irrelevant to ask whether Euclid was right or wrong in introducing his parallels postulate into his geometry. He merely made an assumption and showed what would logically flow from it. If Euclid thought that his proposition was the only possible one in relation to reality, then he would of course have been wrong; but nowhere does he say this. He will have known well enough that the Earth was not flat and that his plane geometry in its application to the physical world was at best an idealization; his geometry is based upon definitions which are as abstract as anyone could wish – points which have no magnitude, lines which have no breadth, planes which have no thickness.

It this is a correct assessment of Euclid's beliefs, does this not conflict with the earlier observation that his geometry, right from its very beginnings, had been more or less identified with reality? Such a conclusion would not be valid. The reputation of infallibility which Euclid's geometry, like other dogmas, had assimilated was in fact acquired over the whole span of its two thousand undisputed years. While the Greeks regarded geometry as an emanation of reality, this was a reality not so much in the practical sense of what actually exists in the world, but rather an undefined and mystical reality or absolute truth as exemplified in the material and spiritual significance which they ascribed to cardinal numbers.

The message of geometry imperceptibly changed over the centuries just as some verbal message may finally reach its destination in a garbled form. Euclid could not choose his disciples. Their interpretation cannot be laid at his door.

Euclid's postulate leads to the geometry of the plane. For a representation of Lobachewsky's geometry we need to consider the very strange and unlikely curved surface of the pseudosphere, so called by Beltrami who first discovered that this representation was possible. This is illustrated in Fig. 49.

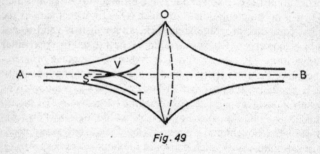

Fig. 49

The pseudosphere results from the revolution of a curve, known as a tractrix, about a line which is its asymptote – that is, which it continuously approaches. In Fig. 49, the tractrix is the curve consisting of the curves AO and OB; its asymptote is the line AB.

V is a point on the surface of the pseudosphere and ST is a given line. Two lines are drawn through V. All these lines are curved, but each has the special property of being the shortest route between any two points on itself, just as the straight line in Euclidean geometry has the selfsame property on a plane surface. Both the lines through V approach ST but will never intersect it. These lines have the same properties in reference to the surface of the pseudosphere as parallel straight lines have in Lobachewsky's geometry.

It may be easy to accept that the lines through V are parallel to ST in the sense indicated above, but there is still one difficulty of interpretation to overcome. These lines are curved. That being so, how can they also be 'straight' lines? This apparent contradiction may best be explained in relation to yet another curved surface – the sphere. This is a shape which, because of our relative familiarity with it, can help us to ease our understanding of the principles involved.

The sphere does not have any of the properties peculiar to Lobachewsky's geometry. We must look instead to another quite different brand of non-Euclidean geometry. This was the brainchild of Bernhard Riemann. In 1854 he proposed, not like Euclid that there is one parallel line, nor like Lobachewsky that there are at least two parallel lines which can be drawn through one and the same point, but that there are no parallel lines at all!

Lobachewsky and others had considered this proposition and had found that, if taken in conjunction with Euclid's other assumptions, it would lead to contradictions. Riemann saw this also, and he promptly discarded another of Euclid's postulates as well. This was the second postulate: 'a straight line may be produced to any length in a straight line'. If we can dispense with Euclid's fifth postulate then, Riemann declared, we can also dispense with the second – or rather, perhaps, interpret it differently.

If we commence a journey at a point on the equator and follow the line of the equator around the world we can, subject only to physical disabilities, continue the journey indefinitely. When we have circled the world once we would, of course, on the subsequent circuits be covering our previous route. The equator, like any other circle, is of finite length but is also endless in the sense that it is unbounded. It has no real starting or finishing point, like the English winter which, according to Byron, ends in July only to recommence in August.

Riemann conceived the idea that straight lines might somehow be supposed to have this same re-entrant property, and he found that this supposition would lead to another self-consistent geometry. This is in many respects quite unlike both Euclid's and Lobachewsky's geometry.

The plot thickens! Riemann's assumptions are apparently more outrageous than Lobachewsky's. Not only are there to be no parallel lines at all, but straight lines double back on themselves; and if there was one thing about which everyone was previously quite certain of straight lines, it was that they did not do that. The assumption leads to no contradictions, but it does lead to some very unexpected theorems.

In Riemann's geometry the sum of the interior angles of any triangle is greater than 180°, whereas in Lobachewsky's geometry it is always less than 180°. Two of the strangest theorems, perhaps, are that all the perpendiculars to a given straight line, if sufficiently produced, but still finite in length, will meet in one point; and that two straight lines similarly produced will enclose an area.

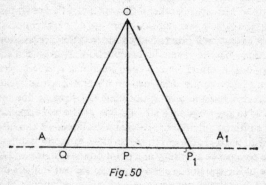

Fig. 50

Fig. 50 is intended to assist in an appreciation of the nature of Riemann's assumptions but it is subject to the same reservation as was necessary in regard to Fig. 49. Non-Euclidean concepts cannot be satisfactorily represented on a flat sheet of paper.

P is any point on the straight line AA_1 while O is any point in the same plane but not on AA_1 and OP is the perpendicular on

AA_1 from the point O. As P moves in the direction of the arrow, so OP will move about O but will always remain in contact with AA_1 and will not, as in Lobachewsky's geometry, approach a limiting position. Every straight line through O will intersect AA_1.

The diagram cannot indicate the way in which OP will move about O but, as we shall see later, if we take AA_1 as having the same properties as an arc of the earth's equator, then OP can be taken as if it has properties similar to those of part of a line of longitude (O being the pole, and P being the point of intersection with the equator). A full rotation of OP would then generate a hemisphere. Line OP_1 as well as OP can then be visualized as being perpendicular to AA_1 and the line OP would, on re-entering our diagram (which covers only a very small part of the whole) assume positions such as OQ before returning to its original position.

This illustration is intended merely to give an idea of the basic concept in Riemann's geometry. This, however, brings us back to the fact that all the lines of a pseudosphere as well as all those on a sphere are curved. How can these also be called straight lines?

First we must be sure that we know what we mean by 'straight' and then we must ascertain whether our notion of this necessarily fixes its nature. How can we define a straight line other than by its straightness? Euclid defined a straight line as that which lies evenly between its extreme points, but this does not really tell us what a straight line actually is. Many definitions have been attempted and the most common one is 'the shortest distance between two points'.

The modern view is that we cannot define geometrical concepts unless we accept the so-called definitions to be no more than assumptions or to be based on such assumptions. We have already noted that, when it came to defining the indefinable abstract, Euclid was naturally no more able to do this than are we.

Whichever definition we choose for a straight line we are still involved with the assumption that the line can behave in the way defined and this assumes also the existence of a plane in which the line can lie. Consequently, when Euclid defines a plane as that which has only length and breadth and in which the straight line between two points in it lies wholly within it, he is really telling us no more than a general property of all surfaces.

A plane is one particular kind of surface. A more general definition of a straight line in any surface might be 'the shortest distance between two points in the surface such that the line lies wholly within the surface'. The use of the word 'straight', however, offends our sense of propriety since it is unalterably identified with the particular straight line of the plane. We call the generalized straight line, for any type of surface, a geodesic instead.

The geodesic in Euclidean geometry is the familiar straight line. The geodesic of a sphere is the great circle, this being a circle whose centre is also the centre of the sphere. The earth is very nearly spherical and its great circles are represented by the meridians or lines of longitude and an infinity of other circles which conform to the same properties as these.

Another paradox is now revealed. What is the shortest distance between London and Dortmund which are close to one line of latitude 51° 30′? It would seem that the shortest journey would be along this line of latitude, but this is not so. The distance measured along a line of latitude is not the shortest distance between two points on the line because latitude lines, other than the equator, are not great circles – their centres do not coincide with the centre of the earth. The shortest distance between the two towns will be along the great circle on which they both lie.

By using the general concept of geodesics instead of the restricted plane straight lines, we can fit Riemann's geometry to the sphere. The sides of triangles in this geometry will, of course, be arcs of geodesics which are curved.

In Fig. 51 the arcs, NAS and NBS, of two great circles through the poles N and S have been drawn as representatives of the infinite number of great circles which pass through those points. It will be appreciated that an infinite number of great circles can also be drawn through any two diametrically opposite or antipodean points on the surface of a sphere. In plane geometry only one line can be the shortest distance between two points. In Riemannian geometry, as on the sphere, there is an infinite number of geodesics which share the property of being the shortest distance between antipodean points. This must be the paradox supreme.

All great circles, which are of the same finite length although boundless, intersect each other and there are therefore no parallel geodesics. Circles of latitude are equidistant but are not geodesics.

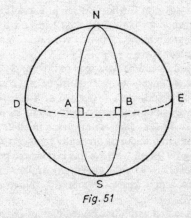

Fig. 51

All great circles through N and S intersect the great circle DE (which on the earth would represent the equator) at right angles. Conversely all the perpendiculars to DE will intersect at N and S. Every two great circles passing through the same poles will enclose a surface area between them – in the diagram such an area is that of the shape bounded by the arcs NAS and NBS. The interior angle sum of the triangle NAB is greater than 180° since the angles at A and B together sum to 180°.

All these are assumptions or theorems derived from Riemann's geometry which fits the surface of the sphere just as the geometry of Lobachewsky was found to fit the surface of the pseudosphere. It is important to realize that they were not invented for these specific purposes. They were developed as logical systems from stated assumptions. All that has been done in relating them to particular surfaces is to have found an application for each of them. They may have other applications.

It is as well to note too that Euclidean geometry itself is not restricted entirely to plane figures but may be applied to some curved surfaces. It is a simple matter to demonstrate this by drawing a triangle on a piece of paper and then wrapping the latter around the curved surface of a cylinder. If the triangle is large enough, parts of it may be made to overlap each other. The triangle is not deformed in any way except that its sides become arcs of curves instead of Euclidean straight lines. These lines are, however, still geodesics between points lying on them and the interior angle-sum remains $180°$ – two more examples of invariance in mathematics.

Any surface which can be 'wrapped or unwrapped' in this way will have a Euclidean geometry. The surface of a cone is another example of such a surface. The surface of a sphere cannot be treated in this way since it is 'everywhere round' as distinct from the surface of a cylinder which is not curved in all its dimensions. A Euclidean straight line can theoretically be drawn directly on to a cylinder along its length whereas this is nowhere possible upon a sphere. This explains why the geography of the world, which is an oblate sphere, cannot be exactly reproduced in its entirety on a flat map.

So we are presented with three quite different geometries and a number of others which can be formed at will merely by adopting different but self-consistent assumptions. We thus have a choice, but it is not a choice of candidates as allegedly representing absolute truths; it is a much more compromising choice of suitability and convenience. If the geometry fits an application, we use it; where more than one geometry gives closely similar results, for example within restricted areas, we use the geometry which is more easily put to work, and this is often Euclidean. Strange as it may seem, however, Riemannian geometry appears to fit observed data of the universe better, and Einstein's relativity theory employs this form.

The impact and implications of these different geometries were to have a startling effect upon the human understanding of the real nature of mathematics. While Euclid was king, everyone concerned with geometry was quite clear what geometry was. Now that Euclidean geometry is seen to be but one of a Federation of structures, the question as to what geometry really is has become much less easy to answer. The answer, if there is one, to such a question depends first upon the even more difficult question as to what is mathematics. We shall return to this conundrum in the final chapter.

13. Many Dimensions

The release of geometry from its inhibitions was symptomatic of a wider though gradual change in man's approach to mathematics. The resultant breaching of the restraining walls, which had barred the way to progress, helped to clear away at least some of the misconceptions and to classify many other problems which had suffered from similar disabling entanglements.

Of these problems one outstanding example is provided by the controversy which had surrounded the concept of a fourth dimension. Four-dimensional geometry was developed as a purely logical and theoretical structure unhampered by the realities of physical space, but it was to be sadly misinterpreted outside the sanctuaries of mathematics.

To many people the mere idea of a fourth dimension was absurd – and it is quite understandable that this should have been so. Intuition does not concede defeat so easily. Others, who tried to explain how such a dimension might be possible, resorted to analogies and science-fairy fictions which were as unsuitable as they were irrelevant. These were acceptable only to those who were already prepared to admit the possibility of a fourth dimension; to those who could not see this possibility, the analogies merely introduced extraneous matter which made a fourth dimension seem even more improbable.

The subject of the fourth dimension created a lively stir in popular opinion although it is doubtful whether more than a few individuals had any true understanding of its implications. Nevertheless the public spirit, once aroused and intrigued by the mystery of a new dimension, seized upon it with high enthusiasm. All at once it was the fabulous crock of gold of another existence;

if only we could find this other dimension it must certainly lead us to the unravelling of the universe!

Many surprising theories were advanced as to the nature of the fourth dimension or of the space which was four-dimensional. Not the least remarkable of these was the theory of Zöllner who held that all our dear departed would eventually be discovered in such a space – a kind of combined Elysium and Valhalla. Nobody suggested that this might also be where the flies went in the winter time, but this would not have been any more remarkable.

For some strange reason, perhaps because of its tantalizing unattainability, a fourth dimension seemed to be a philosophic desirability if not an actual psychological necessity. Many mathematicians too, were just as intrigued by the unknown attributes of outer space, for although mathematics had been relieved of its self-imposed obligation to physical reality, mathematicians not unnaturally retained a strong interest in the latter.

One of the interesting aspects of this subject derives from the question of why anyone should have thought of a fourth dimension at all and why, having thought of this, a fifth dimension was not also demanded. Here we must again differentiate between the logical concepts of mathematics and the intuitive concepts of physical space. In 1843 Cayley in fact extended geometry to n-dimensions (where n is any positive integer) whereas intuition of physical space stopped short at three actual and one potential dimensions.

When Einstein formally recognized time as a fourth dimension in his concept of space-time this was immediately accepted by the popular vote. The fact that time had been regarded in mechanics as a kind of fourth dimension, although in a rather different way, before Einstein appropriated it was immaterial. By accepting the notion now one could claim some incidental personal inkling of the theory of relativity. So it was time, all the time! Thus was the public conscience satisfied, although the anticipated crock of gold remained as fabulous as its legendary leprechaun attendants.

The possibility of a fourth dimension can be advanced only by analogy, but this can be effected in a number of different ways, the total effect of which is to give a vague uneasiness either that there really is a fourth dimension in space which we have not been able to discover or that it is a reproach upon nature for not having one.

A point has no magnitude and, therefore, no dimension; a line has one dimension – length; a plane has two dimensions – length and breadth; a solid has three dimensions – length, breadth and depth. This suggests a progression. Why stop there?

A moving point will trace out a line; a moving straight line will sweep out an area in a plane; a moving plane will generate a solid. Here is another progression. Should not a moving solid generate some other higher dimensional geometrical form, even though the appearance of what such a super-solid would look like is beyond our imagination? Helmholtz commented that the representation of such an object is as impossible as is the representation of colour to one born blind.

Again if we erect perpendicular co-ordinate axes in a plane we can represent any point in the plane by *two* numbers. If we erect a third axis which is perpendicular to both of the other axes, we can represent any point in space by *three* numbers. It is tempting to muse whether we can erect a still further axis which is perpendicular to each of the other three axes and so be able to represent every point in some four-dimensional system. Centuries before Descartes introduced his co-ordinate geometry Ptolemy had pointed out that it was possible to draw three mutually perpendicular lines in space but that a fourth perpendicular, assuming it to be possible, would be without measure or depth – which is the same as saying he thought it not possible.

A further analogy was drawn from the geometrical progression of the form

$$a \quad a^2 \quad a^3 \quad a^4 \quad \ldots$$

If a represents the measurement, in suitable units, of a straight line, then a^2 represents the area of a square of side a; and a^3 represents the volume of the cube of which that square forms a face; surely then a^4 represents the measure of something too? If it represents some geometrical form, of which the cube forms some kind of boundary and if, as is undoubtedly true, this cannot be correctly reproduced in three dimensions, does this not point to the existence of four dimensions?

These various analogies seem at first to give substance to each other, but a closer scrutiny shows that they merely represent different aspects of a single analogy. Each emphasizes a limited numerical progression and is based on an expectation, whether explicit or implicit, that these numbers might be the terms of a longer arithmetic progression.

The analogy is essentially mathematical and an awareness of this fact will warn us that it cannot be expected to lead to any valid conclusion as to the dimensions of physical space. For, as we have seen, mathematics has a law unto itself, as indeed also has space.

A more literary form of the analogy will take us on a tour of inspection of the undesirable territories of Flatland. Here we shall encounter a different emphasis in the analogy and although this is based on weird untenable assumptions it nevertheless provokes some serious thought. It is worth studying to see just how far the analogy itself is successful and also to ascertain the conclusions, if any, which it warrants. It contains at least one inspired feature which cannot fail to excite a response from that indefinable sense of delight which so peculiarly belongs to mathematical imaginativeness.

Flatland is an imaginary two-dimensional universe invented by Dr E. A. Abbott in a book of that name. We are asked to imagine a universe inhabited by two-dimensional beings and it is suggested that their inability to conceive a third dimension is analogous to our inability, should a fourth dimension exist, to conceive such a dimension higher than our own.

The inhabitants of Flatland are of course themselves flat and have shapes familiar in plane geometry. The lowest forms of male life are triangles and the high priests are circles. Intermediate classes have their separate representations while the ladies, for some inexplicable reason, are mere lines. These are the lowest forms of life, and one of the unexpected results of the book's publication was that Dr Abbott was accused of being a woman-hater!

One can imagine the embarrassing situation which would arise in such a universe. If we draw a square, a line and a circle, on a piece of paper, this being the closest representation we can have of a plane, and hold it at eye level so that it is parallel to the ground, all these separate figures, if they are visible at all, will look like straight lines since we shall be able to see only their leading edges. Similarly, so Dr Abbott assured us, the inhabitants of Flatland could see nothing but straight lines. Everyone would in fact look like a woman to everybody else and they would have to resort to the sense of touch to identify each other.

Such a fixation hardly justifies the accusation that Dr Abbott was a misogynist. It would certainly lead eventually to a distressing state of affairs but, fortunately perhaps for public morals, the necessity for such dubious methods of recognition is based upon a fallacy. To be visible at all a body must have three dimensions – two are not enough. Any two-dimensional being we may supposedly imagine as living in a plane would be as abstract as the plane itself. It is just not possible to see a mathematical plane and there is no justification for assuming it to have a physical existence.

It would be opportune here to make it clear that Dr Abbott's little book made no pretence to reproduce mathematical niceties. Bertrand Russell has suggested that the book was meant as a joke. Dr Abbott, however, in his preface to the second edition, besides expressing surprise at the interest which the book had aroused, expressed the hope that it would be of interest to those 'moderate and modest minds' who were prepared to refrain from dogmatic assertions either that a fourth dimension is or is not a fact of existence. The purport of his story is that we shall never know. Any emphasis here upon its oddities or inconsistencies should not imply that his fable is being taken too seriously. These seeming paradoxes are noted and commented upon to demonstrate that analogy can often be over-persuasive when it masquerades as quasi-logic.

Dr Abbott was made aware of the objection that if a Flatlander sees lines then these must have a dimension in height as well as in length and breadth. In his preface to the second edition he admits the facts on which the objection is based but denies its conclusions. Flatlanders do, he says, have a third dimension, but it is totally beyond their perception as a dimension. He slyly points out that it is precisely because all lines look to be exactly the same infinitesimal height that, while this implies the existence of a height dimension, it also deprives the Flatlander of any clue to the concept of such a dimension.

Here he is trying to have the best and is getting the worst of both his worlds in something of an analogical cycle. He resorts to an analogy from the assumed properties of a three-dimensional world to support his analogy of a two-dimensional world which itself is supposed to lead to a conclusion concerning the assumed properties of the three-dimensional world.

Even if this were not so, his second thoughts on the possession of an unrecognizable third dimension within Flatland directly contradict the basic assumption that Flatland is two-dimensional. Whether Flatlanders would be able to discern all their dimensions is thus immaterial. They may not know whether they are two or three dimensional, but Flatland itself must be either two or three dimensions – it cannot be both.

Many of the peculiar aspects of life in Flatland depend upon the common ability of the inhabitants to see their fellow beings. Although this seems to contradict the original assumption of two dimensions we can, perhaps, imagine that they can see in some unexplained manner. Otherwise, Dr Abbott's whimsy collapses at once and this would be a pity because it still has something of interest to offer.

Life is extremely complicated in Flatland because everything looks like a straight line. Even their houses look like this, and have no roofs since these would apparently call for another dimension. When the doors are closed the inhabitants are secure within their walls, happy in the knowledge that the intimate details of their domestic life cannot be observed.

This state of affairs is then used to show that, although their fellow Flatlanders would not be able to see either through or over the walls, nevertheless dwellers in a three-dimensional space of which the two-dimensional world is a part, would be able to look down into the houses just as we may certainly look down on the interior of a doll's house when the roof has been lifted. Then by analogy it is suggested that there may be a four-dimensional space in which the closed surfaces of our three-dimensional world would somehow appear open.

Dr Abbott describes the dream of a Flatlander in which the latter imagines himself visited by a sphere from some three-dimensional space which is quite beyond his conception. He cannot see or gain any idea of the sphericality of his visitor. He can see only within his own plane so that, when the sphere in an attempt to reveal himself passes through the plane, all that the Flatlander is able to see (and he should not really be able to see so much) is the appearance of a point which grows into a circle of increasing size only to decrease again and disappear as the sphere finally passes right through the plane.

The Flatlander cannot watch the motion of the sphere. He sees only a circle which he takes to be a high priest behaving in a manner quite unsuited to the priesthood. It is all utterly incomprehensible to him and all attempts to describe to him the features of a three-dimensional world are appropriately received with a flat denial of such possibilities.

This movement of the sphere is Dr Abbott's greatest inspiration. It is an elegant conception in the best mathematical sense since it provides with great economy of expression, an aesthetically satisfying demonstration that, viewed from different-dimensional worlds, the phenomena of physical space would appear in quite different guises. What would be conceivable in one world would be inconceivable in a world of lower dimensions. Even if we live in a four-dimensional space we would, because of our restriction to a three-dimensional world, view all its phenomena as three-dimensional ones and so conclude that space itself is three-dimensional.

The movement of the sphere has been interpreted as indicating that Dr Abbott had stumbled upon one of the principles of relativity theory. The Flatlander, it has been suggested, would attribute to growth (of the circle) relative to time what the inhabitant of a three-dimensional space would attribute to motion (of the sphere). Similarly, it is possible that those changes in phenomena which we in turn attribute to the flow of time might be due to the motion of the planet, on which we live, relative to a four-dimensional space. Dr Abbott himself does not appear to have realized that this was implicit in his example.

The sphere takes his Flatlander friend to a three-dimensional space to show him what he was missing. The latter's absence causes his wife some consternation and, on his return, he proffers the lame excuse that he had fallen through the trap-door in their floor. Dr Abbott seems to have fallen into his own trap. Into what dimension did the hapless Flatlander fall? If he can have a cellar, why cannot he have a roof? By now we have assumed so much, so if we allow him an abstract plane in which to live perhaps we might also permit him an abstract cellar into which to fall.

Since the Flatlanders' homes are open to inspection by beings in the three-dimensional world it has been suggested that the latter could remove objects from inside the house and make them reappear outside. This would be achieved to the mystified consternation of the Flatlanders since, during the object's transition from one place to another, it would be in a dimension of which they had no knowledge.

This idea extended, as it has been, by analogy to the different conditions in our own three-dimensional world requires that we be prepared for some very strange conclusions. If there is a fourth dimension in which our three-dimensional surfaces are no longer closed then it would be in the direction of this dimension in which our walls would be supposed not to extend. Individuals, assisted by intervention from the four-dimensional space, might disappear from locked rooms into the new dimension; the yolks of eggs might be removed without breaking the shells and the problem of how the milk gets into a coconut would be replaced by the problem of how to keep it in.

This, however, is in the realm of fantasy. It might all be true if there were another dimension; it contributes nothing to the proposition that this other dimension exists. Nobody has ever encountered matter which is less than three-dimensional. In a plane the so-called closed perimeters of houses can themselves be mere abstractions; they cannot be closed in the same sense as can houses of bricks and mortar. It is also worthy of note that when the Flatlander, convinced now by the revelations of his dream that there are indeed three dimensions, attempts to explain this to his fellows, he is for his heresy properly incarcerated in prison from which, for all his newly won knowledge, he remains singularly unrescued.

So ends our brief outline of the saga of Flatland. Despite its inconsistencies and its too many overtaxing assumptions, without which indeed it could never have been written, its overall effect is what Dr Abbott apparently desired. He makes no claim either that there is or that there is not a fourth physical dimension. He shows that it is not within our capacity either to affirm or to deny its existence.

It is curious that higher mutually perpendicular physical dimensions should have been thought to exist at all and that those analogies which have been forthcoming usually emphasize the assumed possibility of such an existence. Rarely if ever is the magic lantern of analogy focused on the converse proposition that there is no reason to suppose that higher physical dimensions should exist. This doubtless arises from the element of romantic invention in the analogies. It is much more satisfying to read about the possible existence rather than the possible non-existence of mythical lands. Jack the Giant-Killer would lose his glamour if the youthful readers of his exploits were to be convinced of the impossibility of his beanstalk's existence.

Dr Abbott was not the first to suggest analogies between our three-dimensional world and worlds of lower dimensions. Helmholtz in a lecture in 1870 used the same general analogy to make intelligible the nature of non-Euclidean spaces. Gauss, too, is on record as having voiced such an analogy, although it is doubtful if he intended it to be taken seriously because he qualified the assumption by the witticism that he had put aside certain difficult problems of geometry, which he hoped he would be able to solve later when he had attained the supposed higher dimensional existence!

Gauss almost certainly did not conceive a two-dimensional world in all the detail which Abbott lavished upon it. Although the latter's work has a bearing on mathematics it is basically a work of literature and the mathematics tends to get lost beneath a spurious coat of pseudo-reality. This is a direct result of mixing mathematical abstractions with supposedly possible analogous physical phenomena. Analogy to lower dimensional physical worlds assumes that these exist in reality not merely as mathematical abstractions. If Abbott convinces us of anything at all, it is that the existence of lower dimensional worlds is well-nigh impossible. If we cannot truly imagine two-dimensional beings, this is of no help whatever in trying to imagine four-dimensional ones. It does not always simplify a problem merely by reducing the numbers.

The value of Abbott's book, whether intentionally planned or not, is its demonstration of the lack of wisdom in confusing physical and abstract considerations. Even if it poses more problems of detail than it resolves, the book nevertheless removes them from the vague encircling clouds of metaphysics and makes them stand out to be recognized. We have dealt with the physical aspects of the analogy at some length in order to dispel some of its illusions. It is all too often presented in so uncritical a manner as to suggest that it is entirely valid. It should not be quoted at all unless its implications and consequences are also stated.

Nevertheless, provided analogy is confined entirely within mathematical abstract thought, we can indeed have as many dimensions in our store cupboard as we like. How does this come about?

It is sometimes said to be preposterous to think about a fourth dimension at all because it is an entirely imaginary concept. This alone does not make it preposterous. Points, lines, planes and other abstractions are just as imaginary and mathematics could not do without them. It is remarkable how easily the mind reconciles itself to abstractions of lower dimensions since the only set of dimensions within our physical experience is threefold. Even Zeus reckoned only with two dimensions, for the Omphalos, the legendary navel of the world, was sited at Delphi by his ingenious if over-simplified idea of despatching two eagles in opposite directions to the far ends of the world. The point at which they met on return, having flown with great discipline at equal speeds – thought Zeus, who perhaps might have been expected to know anyway – was clearly the middle of a line drawn between the ends of the world.

Yet, although we accept lower dimensional forms without demur, we cannot intuitively accept four or more dimensions. Perhaps it offends our pride to think of higher dimensional orders. Perhaps, also, at some time in the future the geometries of higher dimensions will be more readily acceptable in the same way as some of Stravinsky's music, which was enthusiastically booed when first presented to an unsuspecting audience, now appears almost conventional against the modern backdrop of Schoenberg's atonalities and electronic music-making. New generations more easily absorb the new ideas of the eras into which they are born.

The first thing to be clear about is that dimension, as it is generally understood, is a matter of mathematical convention. It is nowadays discussed within reference frames such as those made available by Descartes' co-ordinate geometry. Any point in a plane may be identified by two numbers referring to the x and y axes respectively of a co-ordinate system. Fermat and Euler extended co-ordinate geometry to three dimensions by adding a third axis in depth perpendicular to both the x and y axes, so that any point in a three-dimensional space may be identified by three numbers referring to these three axes.

These are particular dimensions chosen for a specific purpose. They are mathematical dimensions which formalize the intuitive conception of length, width and breadth. Yet plane figures, for example, have more than two dimensions and solids have more than three dimensions in the wider sense of combined distances, directions and positions. A square has a diagonal which is measurable neither as length nor as breadth, but the measurement of this diagonal is as much a representative dimension as are these other two measurements.

Why do we regard the x and y axes in a rectangular co-ordinate system as indicating the only recognized directions of dimensions? Why is the dotted line in Fig. 52 not treated as a dimension of the point A when it is in fact a measurable dimension just as are the x and y segments, its only difference being that it extends in a different direction from the origin? In this sense there are an infinite number of dimensions through the point O, or through any other point, lying within the plane. There are also an infinite number of dimensions through any point in any direction within our three dimensional space – as for example the dimensions represented by all the diameters of a sphere.

Space, so far as we can tell, extends in all directions and this dimensional multiplicity is reflected in the alternative system of polar co-ordinates, which has been shown in reference to Fig. 40 (Chapter 10). This system, which dispenses with the direct use of the notion of rectangular axes, although it is based on their properties, is often used in higher mathematics. Rectangular axes are more often employed in many instances, however, because they are simpler and more convenient to use. This is why they are used; they are not used because they are the right axes to use, since no dimension can be any more right than another.

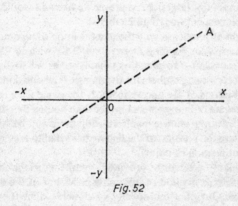

Fig. 52

Rectangular axes enable us to identify a point in space with great simplicity and, because we can do this by reference to three numbers which indicate measurements of its distances or dimensions relative to the axes, space is regarded as three-dimensional. This dimensionality is therefore a purely mathematical concept. It is paradoxical that we define this dimensionality of space by reference to our ability to locate a point which has no physical dimension.

It should also be noted that before we can identify the point in space we first assume the availability of a suitable co-ordinate system. How do we locate the point which is the origin of such a system. Where in space do we erect the axes?

Let us consider two points in space. A is within a particular plane; B is not. If we construct rectangular co-ordinates within that plane we shall require only two numbers to be able to identify A. To identify B, however, we shall have to erect a third axis perpendicular to the plane and will require three numbers. If, however, we construct our original plane axes in the plane containing B, the number requirements will be reversed. Which arrangement is right or, as it might have been put in music-hall cross-talk, where is here? Wherever we draw our co-ordinates we shall, relative to that particular system, require at most three numbers to be able to locate each and every point in space. In fact we can set up the system wherever we like and would choose the most convenient way of doing this.

We might also well ask why the identification of a point should be the criterion for defining dimensions. If we wish to identify a line segment relative to plane rectangular axes we shall require four numbers – two numbers for the fixing of the position of each of the end-points of the line segment. If the plane were regarded as an aggregate of line segments rather than points, then it would be treated as four-dimensional. It will, however, be observed that to obtain the position of the line we have had to take recourse to the identification of points.

Co-ordinate geometry provided mathematicians with a brilliantly simple method of obtaining order out of the chaos of point-space. Out of a multiplicity of possible dimensions they were enabled to reduce the number of significant dimensions to the very minimum. It is this minimum which defines dimensionality. It is curious that the facility thus offered should have accelerated the desire for more rather than less significant dimensions. This seems rather like asking a shopkeeper for his cheapest brand and then asking why he has not got something more expensive.

When Descartes invented his system of co-ordinates he also in effect began the geometrization of algebra, and the algebraization of geometry. This mutual arrangement was of immense benefit to mathematics. It demonstrated the relationship which exists between different processes in the separate subjects but, more importantly perhaps, it showed that analogues of the ideas of one subject might, when applied to the other subject, open up entirely new paths of discovery. Algebra in particular gained from this conjoining of interests and also from the facility with which the simpler geometrical vocabulary could be used in discussing algebraic problems. Not surprisingly therefore, since a good deal of the development of other mathematical concepts were suggested by geometrical properties and since the visual conceptions of geometry when applied to algebra make the latter seem less abstruse, many of the geometrical terms were carried over in connection with these new concepts.

A simple algebraic function can be described by its curve relative to plane co-ordinate axes; a function in three variables may be represented relative to a three-dimensional co-ordinate system. Each of these functions has an algebraic form irrespective of our ability or inability to represent them geometrically. Algebraic functions in two or three variables are associated with geometries of two and three dimensions respectively. Similarly functions in four variables can exist algebraically even though we cannot represent them in a geometrical form relative to perpendicular axes. We exhaust our geometrically representative dimensions more quickly than we run out of equivalent algebraic functions.

Nevertheless we transfer to such functions in four or more variables the same geometrical concepts and terminology as we use for the functions in fewer variables. The geometry of four dimensions is really the algebra of four variables expressed and treated in geometrical fashion. These algebraic variables may have no obvious connection with the physical properties which we associate with the idea of dimension in the ordinary applications of geometry to the physical world.

This seemingly curious way of talking geometrically about things not strictly geometrical was common in ancient Greek times, and it has been suggested that our continued propensity to discuss analysis in this way may merely be evidence that we have failed to grow up. What is certain, however, is that this constitutes a convenient way of talking and thinking; it is a mental expedient for the purpose of clarifying our understanding.

Geometrical language is itself giving way in some aspects to set language because of the realization that the concept of sets is apparently basic to mathematics in general. It really makes no difference what language we speak provided we fully understand, so far as semantics permits, the meanings of the words we use.

The analogies which suggest the possibility of higher dimensions are all numerical or algebraic but are based on the geometric abstractions of points, lines, plane and other elements. These elements, in which the dimensions exist, are abstract as also therefore must be the dimensions themselves. The so-called fourth dimension in physical space is revealed as a will o' the wisp, a figment of misinterpreted mathematical fancy.

Mathematics dissociates itself from such misconceptions but, although the geometries of four or more dimensions are abstract structures they nevertheless do find applications in modern physical theories. In the study of the mechanics of atoms the even more perplexing notion of a geometry in an infinite number of dimensions is used. The theory of relativity is developed upon a particular form of four-dimensional geometry in which time is introduced as a fourth dimension.

One obstacle which bars the way to a proper appreciation of the significance of Einstein's use of time as a dimension is the fact that time is apparently not the same kind of dimension as the well-known trio of length, breadth and height. It is not, like these others, measured in unit of distance, and it is a well-drilled rule of mathematics that only like quantities may be measured by the same units of measurement.

If we try to bring time, measured in seconds, into addition or subtraction of distances, measured in feet, are we not copying the ludicrous behaviour of the jury, at the trial of the Knave of Hearts, who jotted down three dates, added them up and then converted the total to pounds, shillings and pence?

It should perhaps be noted straightaway that time is in fact not regarded as a dimension of space. It is regarded as a dimension of space-time. This distinction may appear to involve a mere play upon words, but this is by no means so. The expression 'space-time' is used for want of a better expression and it is wellnigh impossible to give a direct description of its true meaning with regard to physical reality. It is a mathematical abstract concept which can be described, outside mathematical language, only as a composite concept of which time and space are component elements.

For most of our everyday matters it is usually convenient and often necessary to dissociate time from spatial effects, yet this is never a complete dissociation. We do, however, sometimes, ignore time considerations if we are primarily concerned with spatial dimensions or we ignore the latter when we are mainly interested in the former.

Nevertheless, time considerations are often implicit in spatial measurement. If we are asked to measure the height of a growing plant we must allow for the fact that this height will be different at different times. When we plan to meet a friend under the clock at Victoria Station we must, as well as specifying the spatial dimensions of the meeting place, also specify the time of meeting or we may be there all day.

Einstein's theory reminds us that the analysis of the phenomenon of nature into its supposed separate attributes, of which time and space are but two, is entirely the result of the imaginative thought of man. If we are to aspire to a knowledge of the universe as a whole, it is reasonable to suppose that we must dispense with the artificial distinction between its separate properties. The separate movements of a symphony may have many different characteristics and yet be synthetized into one recognizable and consistent whole.

Although time and space appear to have quite different measurement units it is nevertheless possible to convert units of time into units of distance. Indeed these differing concepts are often conversationally discussed in terms of each other. We may say, for example, that the distance between two railway stations is 120 miles or that the journey between them takes two hours. The journey has two apparently different aspects – the distance covered and the time taken.

There are two important qualifications to make here. Firstly, the supposed measurement equivalence applies only to the rail journey between the two points; the journey by road would take longer. Secondly, it implies a rate of speed which is uniform throughout or which always has the same average value for that distance. The equivalence is thus inexact and therefore unscientific embodying little more than a metaphorical manner of speaking. In dealing with the wider issues of space-time theory we can find an equivalence of measurement unit which is not subject to these qualifications.

One of Einstein's assumptions is that the velocity of light is constant. The velocity is approximately 186,000 miles per second and the constancy of this velocity provides a convenient method for the measurement of astronomical distances in units of time. If the light from a star takes x minutes to reach Earth then its distance from Earth is 11,160,000 x miles. It may well be imagined that the distance travelled by the light from a distant star, if the light were to take a full year to complete the journey, would be truly astronomical! It would be difficult to conceive its immensity, and it would be simpler to say that the star was one light-year's distance from the Earth. In fact, the nearest star, other than the Sun, is about *four* light-years' distance away.

The same basic principle is used on a smaller scale in radar applications. Radio signals, travelling with the same speed as light, are bounced off a target, and the distance of the latter from the transmitter is calculated as the mileage represented by half the time taken by the signal to complete its total return journey.

14. Periods, Elements and Scales

The claim that mathematics need not necessarily have any relation to physical applications seems to imply that mathematics is entirely the invention of man and is not the discovery of natural properties, which the ancient geometers supposed it to be.

Yet as soon as we find an application for our theories we are at once brought to question how physical phenomena first obtained those properties which mathematics appears to describe. Einstein's theory of gravitation dismisses the idea of a force of gravity and suggests that the unhindered paths of moving bodies follow geodesics in the portion of space-time in which they are located. If this is true, is it not remarkable that bodies should comport themselves in this way? What is it, whether a force or whatever, that keeps these on the straight (i.e. geodesic) and narrow path? How is such regularity to be explained?

Nature often seems to forestall us. Indeed, the freedom of mathematics from physical obligations is probably only possible because of the paradox that much of mathematics does in fact have applications to physical phenomena, just as the freedom of a city is possible only because not all men are freemen. Wordsworth, speaking of geometry in particular, found 'both elevation and composed delight...in the relation those abstractions bear to Nature's laws...'

Many of the mathematical theories with physical applications are of a very involved character, but their fascination derives from the discovery in nature of intricate patterns which seem to be based on quite simple number relationships.

This inherent mathematical quality is sometimes manifested

in the behaviour of animals – other than trained circus per-
formers – and insects. In Chapter 9 it was noted that the honey
bees always built their cells in the most economical hexagonal
shape. There is an old saying about 'telling the bees'. Here is
something which they apparently could have told us long before
we discovered it.

One branch of the Eumenes wasp family has been observed to
have the regular habit of supplying its young with five caterpillars
each. Another species supplies ten caterpillars to each of its
young and the interesting fact is that these quantities, except for
failure on the part of the occasional dunce, is constant within
each species. In yet another species the males are smaller
and presumably less voracious than the females; their fond
parents supply the former with five caterpillars and the latter
with ten.

This nice discrimination will scarcely be appreciated by the
caterpillars and may be casually dismissed by human observers as
merely an instinctive action. Whether the wasps can think in the
same way as we do or whether they can not, it is no mean achievement to get the answers right so regularly. For, although it may
be instinctive for the parents to provide different quantities of
food to their offspring, this does not explain how they can be
sure, whether by a form of counting or otherwise, that the rations
are exactly right.

Some creatures have a remarkable time and calendar sense.
Oysters and other shell-fish regulate their lives according to
tidal movements, apparently being possessed of their own built-in
nautical almanac. This may again be instinctive but, if it is, the
wonder of it is not reduced. The wonder is transferred to the
instinct. An awareness of time is not restricted to humans.
Oysters seem to know when the next high tide is due. Any
suggestion that this is communicated to them by the movement
of the water has been dispelled by experiments in which oysters,
moved for inspection to a laboratory tank hundreds of miles away
from their home beds, continued for some while to regulate their
lives by their home tides.

The healthy human heart pulses at a regular rate and its pulse-
beats may be likened to the ticking sounds of a clock. The heart

acts like an inner clock and there are many objects or phenomena which reveal a regular periodic action. We derive our
calculation of the passing of time from the movements of the
earth and the moon. The earth rotates about its axis once in
just under twenty-four hours; the moon revolves around the
earth once very lunar month; the earth revolves around the sun
once very year. It is unfortunate that none of these rotations or
revolutions will fit in tidily with the others and that minor
irregularities do occur, but in their separate ways they reveal a
periodicity of which the action of the clockmaker's prize time-
piece is an analogue.

An atom, in emitting light waves of definite frequency, behaves
with the same kind of regularity as a clock, and some of these
natural clocks are far more reliable than the man-made variety.
The disintegration of radioactive materials has also been shown
to be related to specific periods of time. Radium has a half-life
of approximately 1620 years. That is, half the material will have
disintegrated at the end of that period. Half the remainder will
have disintegrated at the end of a further 1620 years, and so on.
Other radioactive materials have shorter or longer half-lives and
their disintegration appears to be independent of external circumstances. Heating them to intense temperatures or freezing and
other indignities does not seem to affect this regularity which
has been put to practical use in the dating of geological
discoveries.

These are but a few of the many examples which could be
cited. There are many more and probably countless more of
which we have as yet no knowledge.

Reference has already been made to the regularity of atomic
clocks. Atoms have themselves been arithmetized and the
chemical elements which they constitute exhibit most surprising
numerical qualities.

Each element has its own distinctive kind of atom and no other
kind. These distinctive atoms have different masses, and the
atomic weight of an element is a number which represents how
much heavier the distinctive atom of that element is than the
lightest of all the atoms, the distinctive atom of hydrogen.
Dalton, who originated this form of quantitative relationship,

chose hydrogen as having an atomic weight equal to unity. This seemed a logical step in the attempt to simplify calculations, but it was subsequently found to be less convenient than expected and oxygen was chosen as a standard with an atomic weight of 16. Relative to this standard, hydrogen has an atomic weight of 1·008.

In 1865 John Newlands proposed what he provisionally called a law of octaves. He had observed that, if the then known elements were arranged in ascending order of their atomic weights, similar chemical properties recurred after an interval of seven (or a multiple of seven) elements. 'In other words,' he wrote, 'members of the same group stand to each other in the same relation as the extremities of one or more octaves in music'. This was received by many of his contemporaries with high merriment. So absurd did it seem to them that one critic suggested scornfully that he might just as well have arranged the elements in alphabetical order.

Newlands' observation was in fact an over-simplification, yet the basic idea of periodicity, which was at the heart of it, was soon shown to be justified. This periodicity, however, depends primarily on atomic number, rather than on atomic weight, and is not so simple as it first appeared. We shall return to the idea of atomic number later.

In 1869 Mendeleev produced a classification of elements, in ascending order of atomic weight, which showed that elements of equal valency recurred at fixed intervals, the similarity of general chemical properties being in fact implied by this equality.

Mendeleev had two main criteria. The elements should be placed in the order of their atomic weights; and elements with similar general chemical properties should be placed in the same category. For the most part, these criteria involved no conflict but, to a lesser degree, there were two inconsistencies which had to be resolved.

In a few instances the effect of placing an element in the appropriate category, according to its chemical properties, was to reverse the correct order, according to atomic weight, as between two consecutive elements. In some other instances it seemed necessary to leave a few spaces empty since otherwise succeeding elements would have had to be moved from those positions for which, according to the theory, their chemical properties would clearly have qualified them.

Mendeleev was convinced that his theory was correct. Despite these few inconsistencies, the overall pattern seemed so obviously right to him that he refused to let these special instances defeat him. He therefore boldly predicted that the grouping of these items by chemical properties should take precedence over the ordering by atomic weight sequence and, more remarkably, that there must be some elements as then undiscovered which belonged in his empty spaces.

Mendeleev clearly believed in the cliché that attack is the best form of defence. Predictions based upon a theory offer the stiffest test of the truth of the theory. His predictions as to the existence of then unknown elements were to be brilliantly fulfilled. His decision, in conflicting cases, to give priority to chemical properties at the expense of upsetting the atomic weight order was also to be vindicated; although his belief that, in these particular instances, the atomic weights must have been wrongly calculated was not justified in every case.

In his classification a gap appeared in the group headed by the element boron and within atomic weight limits of 40 and 48. Gaps also appeared in the groups headed by the elements aluminium and silicon respectively and within atomic weight limits of 65 and 75. Mendeleev therefore predicted that elements, which he named eka-boron, eka-aluminium and eka-silicon, existed. Since eka-boron was required to be within the atomic weight limits of 40 and 48, he predicted its own atomic weight as 44. Since both eka-aluminium and eka-silicon were required to be within the atomic weight limits of 65 and 75, he predicted their own atomic weights as 68 and 72 respectively.

By 1886 all these predicted elements had been discovered. Eka-aluminium was the first to be identified; it was found in 1875 in a zinc ore mined in the Pyrenees. Eka-boron was found in Scandinavia in 1879. Eka-silicon was identified in 1886 in Freiburg in a silver ore called argyrodite. These elements were given new names: Gallium, Scandium and Germanium respectively.

Their actual atomic weights, shown against Mendeleev's predictions are:

Actual Elements		Predicted Elements	
Germanium	72·6	Eka-silicon	72
Gallium	69·72	Eka-aluminium	68
Scandium	44·96	Eka-boron	44

Mendeleev's other significant assertions were that the then accepted atomic weights of some of the elements were incorrect. When he compiled his table of elements Uranium was thought to have an atomic weight of 119. Mendeleev disputed this because there was no empty space between tin (atomic weight 118) and antimony (122). There was, however, an empty space in the table where its properties would fit it for inclusion. It was subsequently found that the correct atomic weight is 238 (a multiple of 119) and that this fitted neatly into the space suggested by Mendeleev.

Again, indium was thought to have an atomic weight of 76 (a multiple of 38). Mendeleev suggested, and subsequently confirmed, that the correct atomic weight is 114 (another multiple of 38), and this fitted in comfortably in a space appropriate both to this particular atomic weight and to the chemical properties of indium. The atomic weights shown in these two paragraphs are those which were calculated at or before Mendeleev's publication. Calculations now used are more precise and are included here to avoid possible confusion: uranium 238·07; tin 118·70; antimony 121·76; indium 114·82.

There are three blemishes upon the basic arrangement adopted by Mendeleev. According to its chemical properties tellurium should be in a lower group of elements than is indicated by its atomic weight 127·61. On the other hand, iodine should be in a higher group than indicated by its atomic weight 126·91. Mendeleev therefore reversed the order of these two elements, which appeared consecutively in his table, so that each should appear in its appropriate chemical group.

Similarly it is necessary to reverse the numerical order of the atomic weights of cobalt (58·94) and nickel (58·7); and also of argon (39·94) and potassium (39·1) if these elements are to appear in groups appropriate to their chemical properties.

Except for these examples, the order of elements by their atomic weights has remained undisturbed and newly discovered elements have fallen neatly into a revised form of periodic table. Nevertheless these few examples spoil the numerical niceties of the array of elements and, unless they are taken as exceptions which prove the rule (not a wise thing to do in mathematics or anywhere else) they mar the concept on which Mendeleev built his ordered structure.

Nevertheless Mendeleev's order of placing elements has since been confirmed by other criteria in such a way as also to satisfy mathematical consistency. The respective atomic weights indicate the correct position of the elements, apart from the three anomalous instances shown above, in the periodic system. For these anomalous cases, the atomic weights indicate the approximate position of the elements in the system and, in each case, it is necessary only to reverse the order of two consecutive elements.

The order of elements is described numerically by assigning to each space in the periodic table an ordinal number according to its position. This number is called the atomic number of the element which occupies the space, and has been found to have a much greater significance than that implied by its origin as a mere ordinal label. In 1913, Moseley demonstrated that it is characteristic of the physical nature of the element itself.

The electronic bombardment of an element will induce an X-radiation, and Moseley's experiments disclosed that the radiation peculiar to a specific element may be identified by its characteristic wave frequency. Each element has its own particular associated radiation, and each radiation has its own particular wave length and frequency.

Moseley noted that certain measurements consistently fell into regular order. In particular, the square root of the frequencies increased regularly with atomic number. A plot of this root against atomic number produced a straight line, the increments in which were equal for every unit increase in atomic number.

Moseley accordingly concluded that the atomic number of an element must be truly characteristic of its physical structure, and the regularity was so evident that, like Mendeleev before him, he was encouraged to predict the subsequent discovery of elements as then unknown At that time there was no known element in the space between Molybdenum and Ruthenium (atomic numbers 42 and 44 respectively); between Tungsten and Osmium (74 and 76); and between Neodymium and Samarium (60 and 62). Moseley predicted that the unknown elements would have atomic numbers of 43, 61 and 75; these are now known to be Technitium, Promethium and Rhenium respectively.

The significance of the atomic number of an element is in its accepted interpretation as being also the number of electrons in the element's distinctive atom and the number of protons in the atomic nucleus. This interpretation also implies the general chemical character of the element. Mendeleev was in a sense working from symptoms – the chemical behaviour of elements – whereas Moseley showed that this, as also the order derived from it, rests more securely on the fundamental physical structure of the elements.

This throws enlightenment on the interrelated chemical and physical facts of matter. From the purely numerical aspect it is intriguing to ponder the fact that both men could predict the existence of then unknown elements from gaps in a numerical system. Yet here again, although mathematics could point to the apparent absence of elements from the table, nevertheless the remarkable elemental regularity upon which mathematics based its prognosis exists quite independently of mathematics.

It may seem curious that Newlands should have cited the musical system of octaves as providing an example of periodicity of which his atomic weight 'law' was an analogue. Atomic theory is concerned with the basic material fabric of the world whereas music resides ephemerally in the ear of the listener. It might therefore be thought that the analogy should be reversed to give substance to the quality of music.

One man's music is another's noise. There is a wide difference between the types of music developed in the western and eastern hemispheres respectively. The Chinese conception of music, for example, excites very little response other than irritation from European listeners. It is impossible to define music absolutely, but it is a generally accepted convention that it is the art of combining pleasing, regular and smooth sounds of definite pitch by means of concord, rhythm and harmony. This can be but an imprecise description at best for, as Jeans has noted, 'it is regularity which distinguishes music from mere noise', but that 'absolute unending regularity produces mere unpleasing monotony'.

The distinction between what is and what is not musical or harmonious is basically a matter of convention although it tends to become more deeply imbedded into our subconscious than do most conventions of behaviour. Conventions imply standards, and standards imply measurements. Although it is not possible to establish measuring criteria for judging the musical quality of actual compositions, nevertheless it is possible to accept Weyl's claim that all musicians would agree that there is a strong formal, that is mathematical, element underlying the emotional content of music.

Undoubtedly the most remarkable phenomenon of this mathematical element of music is that of the octave which reveals a periodicity much more regular and precise than that suggested in Newlands' atomic weight theory. The octave is itself based upon the remarkable phenomenon of pitch variation. This is difficult to define in terms of received sound, but it may be precisely described scientifically.

All sound is produced by vibration, whether this be the vibration of the strings of a violin, the vibration of a column of air in a wind instrument or the vibration of some other medium. The pitch of a note is the property by which it appears to be high or low relative to other notes and it is measured by the frequency of the vibrations which produce the note. The frequency is the number of complete vibrations in one second.

An increase in the frequency will result in the raising of pitch, while a decrease in the frequency is accompanied by the lowering of pitch. Each note on the musical scale has its own distinctive fixed frequency measurement – fixed, that is, within the scale, although the latter is subject to certain superimposed conventions of musical performance. The placing of the notes of the musical scale relative to the scale of frequency measurements has varied over the years. While this has its effects in the performance of music, it does not alter any of the relationships between individual notes within the musical scale. Once a definite pitch reading has been assigned to a particular note, other notes may be recognized as standing in some simple frequency relation to it.

Pythagoras is credited with the discovery of these simple ratios, to which we shall shortly refer. Pythagoras shared the Greek passion for ratios between whole numbers, because suitable ratios could be employed to relate separate measurements into chains of measurements and it was of particular significance to them that this could be achieved by the inspired properties of whole numbers. A lesser known story about Pythagoras's regard for ratios concerns his calculation of the tallness of Heracles who, according to legend, paced out the athletics stadium at Olympia. Since later Greek stadia were all shorter than the Olympic one, although constructed to the same number of paces of some ordinary mortal, Pythagoras reasoned that the ratio between the stadia lengths was the same as the ratio between the pace-lengths of Heracles and an ordinary man and that the heights of these two would also be in the same ratio.

This is fanciful indeed, but the discoveries of musical ratios by Pythagoras are much more reliable. He noted that whenever a string was divided so as to give two notes which stood in some recognizable relationship to each other, the respective lengths of the string segments were related to each other in a ratio between small integers. The pitch of a string can be altered by changing its tension, length, weight or temperature; but provided these properties are not changed the relationship between the notes produced by the string segments is always the same.

An octave is an interval embracing eight notes, the interval being the difference in pitch between the first and the eighth notes. Greek mythology ascribed the invention of the musical scale of the seven-string lyre variously to Hermes and Apollo. The seven strings of the lyre were believed to stand in some relation to the softer sounds of the seven vowels of the Greek alphabet, and this was in some way supposed to confer upon music a mystical therapeutic quality.

The octave still has seven distinct and different sounding notes, lettered A to G respectively. Notes which are an octave apart, that is the first and eighth notes of an octave, have the same letter-name. The note an octave above C, for example, is also called C; they are distinguished from each other by the addition of a dash, the second note appearing as c^1. This similarity of lettering is retained because notes which are an octave apart seem to the ear to be like the same note sounded at different pitch readings rather than like entirely different notes.

Since notes are said to be distinguished from each other by their pitch readings, the previous statement may seem absurd but, paradox or not, it is nevertheless an undeniable and remarkable fact of acoustics. This is surprising in itself but the mathematical discovery of Pythagoras in relation to the octave was even more surprising. He observed that, for a given note produced by a specific string length, the symmetry of the higher octave was completed by the simple device of halving the string-length. Conversely he could lower the pitch of sound by an octave by doubling the string length.

He also noted that by dividing a string at the two-thirds mark he could raise the pitch by a perfect fifth (interval embracing five notes) and, by taking it at the three-quarters mark, he could raise the pitch by a perfect fourth (interval embracing four notes). Thus, given identical kinds of strings in identical conditions, the string-length ratios for the various intervals were:

Basic note	1:1
Fourth	3:4
Fifth	2:3
Octave	1:2

These ratios, together with others developed by Zarlino, form the so-called natural or diatonic scale. These ratios are shown in Col. 1 of Table A. Once we know the pitch reading for any one note, the pitch of any other note can be calculated by the use of these ratios. The standard pitch is nowadays taken, by international agreement to be based on 440 frequencies for the treble A. The pitch of C^{I} can be calculated by the appropriate ratio

$$\frac{C^{\text{I}}}{A^{\text{I}}} = \frac{3}{5} \text{ whence } 3A^{\text{I}} = 5C^{\text{I}}$$

Substituting A^{I} = 440 in this equation gives C^{I} = 264. These and the other frequencies in the natural scale are shown in Col. 3 of Table A.

TABLE A NATURAL (DIATONIC) AND
TEMPERED (CHROMATIC) SCALES
'Middle C' Octave

			Frequencies	
Natural Scale				
Ratios		*Notes*	*Natural*	*Tempered*
(1)		(2)	(3)	(4)
1:1	1·0	C^{I}	264	261·6
—	—	C♯		277·2
8:9	1·125	D	297	293·7
—	—	D♯		311·1
4:5	1·25	E	330	329·6
3:4	1·333	F	352	349·2
—	—	F♯		370·0
2:3	1·5	G	396	392·0
—	—	G♯		415·3
3:5	1·667	A	440	440·0
—	—	A♯		466·2
8:15	1·875	B	495	493·9
1:2	2·0	C^{II}	528	523·3

Because of the limitations of keyed instruments it is necessary to sacrifice the purity of the natural scale. Whereas a string player may, in theory at least, obtain any note from his strings by suitable fingering, the piano player does not have the same freedom. He is limited to the number of notes equivalent to the number of his keys, each key having its own predetermined note. As a compromise the natural scale is tempered or adjusted by the device of 'equal temperament', to give a chromatic scale in which twelve semitones are included in an octave, there being a constant ratio between the pitch of consecutive semitones. This common ratio is approx. 1·05946.

Again by taking the pitch of A^I as 440, the use of this common ratio enables us to calculate all the other frequencies. These are shown in Col. 4 of Table A. The success of this compromise tempering is illustrated by the closeness of many of the frequency readings in the two tables. The tempered scale is designed so that the frequencies of consecutive notes are in geometric sequence with a common ratio, whereas the frequencies of the natural scale, although related by simple ratios to the fundamental note, do not have either a common ratio or a common difference.

If we now consider several octaves together, the periodicity will appear even more remarkable. If the note C^I has a pitch of 264, then its octave C^{II} has a pitch of twice this magnitude, equal to 528; similarly, the octave of C^{II}, that is C^{III} will have a pitch of 1056. Although we experience two octaves in some way as musical intervals of equal size, nevertheless the frequency ranges of the octaves are not equal although the *logarithms* of the frequencies do increase by equal amounts – a common difference of ·3010.

$$C^I = 264; \log 264 = 2·4216$$
$$C^{II} = 528: \log 528 = 2·7226$$
$$C^{III} = 1056; \log 1056 = 3·0236$$

The pitch of a string is doubled (that is, raised by an octave) by halving the string length. Pitch is also related to the tension of the string; to double the pitch it is necessary to increase the tension fourfold. The number 2 and its powers appear prominently in basic acoustic relationships.

It is said that, in his experiments, Pythagoras used a string which was 12 units in length. Whether or not this was so, it is true that a string of this length would have provided him with results very much to his taste.

By dividing the string at its mid-point (6 units) he could have raised the pitch an octave; at the two-thirds point (8 units) by a perfect fifth; at the three-quarters point (9 units) by a perfect fourth. These integers 6, 8, 9 and 12 are related to each other in remarkable manner by way of the properties of different kinds of mathematical mean values.

Iamblichus noted what he called a 'most perfect proportion' consisting of four terms which had been discovered by the Babylonians. For any values a and b, then

$$a : \frac{a+b}{2} = \frac{2ab}{a+b} : b$$

If we substitute $a = 12$; $b = 6$, we obtain the proportion

$$12:9 = 8:6$$

The intriguing property of this proposition is that 9 is the arithmetic mean of 12 and 6; and 8 is the harmonic mean of 12 and 6. The geometric mean of 12 and 6 is the same as the geometric mean of 9 and 8; and it is therefore also the same as the geometric mean of the arithmetic and harmonic means of 12 and 6.

There is a legend that Pythagoras, passing a blacksmith's forge, noted that four out of the five hammers being used sounded in concord together whereas the fifth sounded a discord. He is then supposed to have weighed the hammers and to have found that the four in-harmony hammers weighed 6, 8, 9, 12 units respectively, whereas the weight of the fifth discord hammer was expressible only by an awkward fraction.

This story may be founded on fact since a trained musical ear, whether belonging to Pythagoras or not – but apparently not to the blacksmith – would be able to observe such effects. On the other hand there may be as little substance in the story, as there is in the story – subsequently proved erroneous – that Handel's *Harmonious Blacksmith* resulted from an enforced sojourn in a smithy during a rainstorm.

The harmonic mean of given numbers is the reciprocal of the arithmetic mean of the reciprocals of those numbers. To calculate the harmonic mean of 6 and 12 we have the arithmetic mean of the reciprocals of these numbers is

$$\left(\frac{1}{12} + \frac{1}{6} \right) \div 2 = \frac{1}{8}$$

and the reciprocal of 1/8 is 8. Thus the harmonic mean of 6 and 12 is 8.

The harmonic mean breaks an ascending octave into two intervals, a fourth (for example, from C to F) and a fifth (F to C'). The word *harmonic*, which the general public now associate most readily with musical matters, originally meant the orderly arrangement of the component parts in a complex structure. Music is one field of application, but harmonic mean values are significant in many other applications.

The harmonic mean is the appropriate form of average to consider when dealing with such diverse matters as speeds and prices. If a car completes two stages of a journey at speeds of 10 m.p.h. and 20 m.p.h. for the separate stages of ten miles each, the average speed for the whole 20 miles is *not* the arithmetic mean of 10 and 20 (i.e. 15) m.p.h. This is a common fallacy. The correct average is given by the harmonic mean of 10 and 20. The arithmetic mean of the reciprocals of these numbers is

$$\left(\frac{1}{10} + \frac{1}{20}\right) \div 2 = \frac{3}{40}$$

The reciprocal of this value, and therefore also the harmonic mean of 10 and 20, is therefore equal to $13\frac{1}{3}$. The average speed over the whole journey of 20 miles is $13\frac{1}{3}$ m.p.h. This can be checked easily since the first 10 miles will take 1 hour; the second 10 miles will take $\frac{1}{2}$ hour; the whole 20 miles will therefore take $1\frac{1}{2}$ hours; the speed is therefore $13\frac{1}{3}$ m.p.h.

We have seen that Newlands' law of octaves for the chemical elements was an oversimplification of a periodic law and that the periodicity of properties implied by atomic number is of a more complex nature. Newlands could not have guessed that the true order of the elements in the periodic table would be determined by a phenomenon which was also fundamental in placing the notes on the musical scale. The concepts of wave theory are common to both. Each element is associated with its distinctive X-radiation wave frequency; each musical note is identified by its distinctive wave frequency.

Pythagoras regarded mathematics itself as a kind of silent music. Sylvester once described music as being the sister to algebra. 'May not Music,' he asked, 'be described as the Mathematic of sense, Mathematic as the Music of reason? Thus the musician feels mathematics; the mathematician thinks music.'

When a musician scans his score, he can 'hear' the music of the notes, just as the reader of poetry can sense the rhythm of unspoken verse. So in mathematics it is possible to appreciate the elegance which underlies its symbols and to enjoy the aesthetic satisfaction which derives from the contemplation of pattern in numbers and of numbers in nature. It is not inappropriate, therefore, that we can also find a pattern of numbers in music.

15. What's it All About?

We have not so-far defined mathematics – and he would be a rash person who attempted to do so. Definition seemed simpler when the structure of mathematics was thought to have recognizable boundaries. But mathematics has outgrown its supposed limitations and is still sturdily growing, thrusting out new branches with the enthusiasm of eternal spring.

If we ask the simple question – 'What is mathematics?' – (a question simple in phrasing but not in implication), the answer, after a great deal of heart searching, is even more simple to state. Philosophers have put forward various theories as to the nature and foundations of mathematics, but the plain fact is that we do not yet know what mathematics really is and, as Newton sadly concluded, we probably never shall.

This may seem to be inconsistent with the avowed merits of mathematical rigour and logic. If we cannot define mathematics itself so as to identify its standards of reliability, how may we justify an insistence that those standards be maintained? Are such standards, if they exist at all, external of mathematics? Are accepted mathematical principles to be regarded as truths of the universe, whether physical or otherwise?

These questions bring us to the centre of the mysterious maze of mathematics. They are not merely questions of whether the ultimate truths of mathematics will ever be revealed to mankind. There is also the question of whether mathematics has anything to do with ultimate truths or not. This may be expressed more directly by asking whether mathematical principles are discovered or invented by man or perhaps engendered in some more hazily mysterious manner. Is mathematics to be regarded as the creative domain of mankind, as are music and art, or as an all-embracing ultimate truth whose principles await discovery by the probe of the mathematician in the same way as the wonders of lost civilizations await the spade of the archaeologist.

This has been a fertile field for philosophical disputations and, although most mathematicians now agree that mathematics is the work of mankind, the red herring of doubt is still to some extent encouraged by the refusal of some parts of mathematics to acknowledge its debt to man. Philosophy, it is true, has no absolute answers upon ultimate truths. It may at best offer opinions and at worst it can come close to warranting Bunthorne's strictures that 'the meaning doesn't matter if it's only idle chatter of a transcendental kind'.

One of the most telling ironies to which natural philosophical judgments have ever been exposed arose in the coincidental discovery of Ceres, the eighth known planet, and the publication of Hegel's scornful and uncompromising assertion that philosophy conclusively demonstrated that there could be precisely seven planets and no more! Most philosophical problems arise out of a perverse insistence upon trying to define the indefinable. We shall not try to do this here, but it is nonetheless fascinating to study the differing points of view which have been advanced.

These can be no more than opinions. They are not definitions and, indeed, definitions are not always helpful to our understanding of the concepts supposedly defined. We might inadequately try to define music as the art of combining sounds with a view to the realization of beauty of form and the expression of emotion, but this alone conveys no idea at all of the sense impressions which music induces. There are also at least three words in the supposed definition which themselves require to be defined!

We have previously noted Euclid's inability to define all the terms he used and we nowadays accept the fact that some terms in any system must necessarily remain undefined. Even when definitions are attempted, however, a new difficulty arises out of the waywardness of words; unless extreme care is exercised the words used may not fully express the ideas intended and may be exposed to differing interpretation risks. Words have a wilfulness of their own, not unlike the independent spirit in which numbers seem to form their own relationships, and they all too often intrude upon the lines of communication between individuals.

There are some clues in the preceding chapters as to the reason for the modern belief that mathematics is the creation of man. This view is of comparatively recent origin; it has not always been so. The Greeks clearly regarded mathematics as being entirely external of man and completely independent of his ability to fathom its depths. In Egypt mathematical knowledge was the jealously guarded prerogative of the priesthood. The Rhind Papyrus, indited by the scribe Ahmed about three thousand years ago, reveals some of the Egyptian methods of arithmetic and is significantly headed 'Directions for Knowing all Dark Things'.

These early origins of a subject, whose sublime mystery we still cannot penetrate, were absorbed into the wider profundities of religious doctrine and thence into philosophy. When mathematics was released from its priestly imprisonment it became the esoteric property of quasi-religious philosophies such as that of the Pythagoreans.

When philosophy moved away from its former dependence upon religion, mathematics moved with it so that individuals who could by no means be described as religious could still discern in mathematical principles the manifestations of absolute truths. Even in the twentieth century, a mathematician of such repute as G. H. Hardy still remained firmly convinced that mathematical reality is external to human thought and that it is merely the function of mankind to discover or observe it.

Hardy was a specialist in pure mathematics – to the eccentric extreme of being completely uninterested in any practical applications whatever. His favourite subject was undoubtedly the theory of whole numbers to which he himself made magnificent contributions. This theory, which is devoted to the study of patterns in number, is peculiarly suited to foster a belief that mathematics cannot be entirely man-made. Even when deprived of the mystical Pythagorean significance, the peculiarities of number relationships are such as to suggest that they at least are independent of human thought.

Mathematics originated in Number. The sequence of whole

numbers was devised or evolved in some way as a simple reference frame for counting. Yet these same numbers exhibit remarkable properties which have no connection with mere counting and were certainly not even suspected in the act of creation or the process of evolution.

The integers, once invented, were soon consorting with each other and pairing off in the most surprising manner. In Ravel's *L'Enfant et les Sortileges* the numbers achieve personalities and, encouraged by an old gentleman in a pi hat, they appear in the form of retribution to mock the child who has misbehaved. Fortunately the integers cannot be personified in this way, but their behaviour is really no less remarkable.

The odd numbers, for example, form up in a kind of infinite square dance, the sum of any series of consecutive odd numbers (whose first term is 1) being always a perfect square. Thus:

$$
\begin{aligned}
1 &= 1 \\
1 + 3 &= 4 \\
1 + 3 + 5 &= 9 \\
1 + 3 + 5 + 7 &= 16
\end{aligned}
$$

All perfect squares, whether odd or even, are included in ascending order of magnitude in the sequence of totals thus formed.

Then for the sake of variety the same consecutive odd numbers form up into different cubist groupings so as to produce all the perfect cubes. That is

$$
\begin{aligned}
1 &= 1 \\
3 + 5 &= 8 \\
7 + 9 + 11 &= 27
\end{aligned}
$$

and so on.

These are very simple examples of number behaviour but they illustrate, as perfectly as could the most abstruse theorem, the fact that numbers have properties which were not wittingly built into the number structure. Certain it is that, no matter how the integers originated, the diversity of their inter-relationships, which appear to be too well patterned to be the result of mere accidental coincidence, could nevertheless hardly have been intentionally designed.

It may also be noted that, while it is undoubtedly more flattering to the intellect of man to suppose that he invented and is still inventing mathematics, physical phenomena quite outside his control nevertheless apparently conform to mathematical principles. Viewing all this apparent order and cohesion in nature, it is difficult not to believe that this involves some intrinsic property akin to mathematics which must have existed for millenia before the advent of man. The mathematical system as we know it is seemingly so much in harmony with nature that it is difficult to dissociate the one from the other.

Yet for all the apparent order in nature, there is as much if not more apparent disorder. The fact that many dimensions of nature may be so remarkably described by mathematics does not necessarily imply that these dimensions are of structures formed to a model derived from the same mathematical system. The use of a camera to photograph physical beauty does not imply that the photogenic quality of the subject was designed for the purpose of being photographed. On the other hand the quality which makes a subject photogenic exists independently of the camera; we may still wonder at those properties of nature which mathematics is able to describe.

The claim that mathematics is the creation, however unmanageable, of man may be thought presumptuous on his part. Yet oddly enough this claim serves to show that man is as far from the ultimate verities as he ever was. Indeed, if the world has as we believe existed for millions of years, it is perhaps even more presumptuous to imagine that we shall ever know anything certain about its origins, mathematical or otherwise.

The restriction of mathematics to the realms of human thought implies that while if it is suitable we may use it to measure some dimensions of the universe, this nevertheless precludes any claim by mathematics to explain the latter. To attempt to confine nature within the logical restriction of man's understanding of it would be absurd. This realization will help us to avoid the mistake of making models of physical phenomena and then ascribing to the latter the properties of the former. We think of the world as almost spherical (although recent opinions have suggested it may be more nearly pear-shaped) and we make little plastic globes to represent it. These globes possess only those properties which we give them; if the seas on the globes really consisted of water, they would soon drain away.

What we call knowledge is fundamentally very much less than we like to think it is, and it depends for its acceptance upon our ignorance of other 'facts' which may conflict with it. Our knowledge of the universe is no more than the interpretation of a mass of observations of events. This inductive process is an essential part of our research, but it has to do with appearances of reality rather than with physical reality itself. It is wrong to ascribe special significance to the events we observe other than is explicit in their occurrence.

Our calendar year is the result of observations of the position of the Earth relative to the Sun. It is not exact in number of days; it takes the Earth approximately 365¼ days to complete one orbit of the Sun. Midnight on New Year's Eve therefore has no precise significance. It may involve a pleasant ritual at a convivial party but, for those who do not like such jollifications, there is no point in sitting up until midnight just to have a drink merely to celebrate the completion of another successful trip around the Sun. The only effect of this would be to make New Year's Day seem greyer than it otherwise might.

The relative positions of the Sun and the Earth express a relationship akin to that of a mathematical ratio. The calendar cannot be used as a proof that the Earth travels round the Sun or vice-versa. Indeed the ancients used the same basic observations to support their theory that the Sun travelled around the Earth. They thought that they could see the Sun move across the sky with apparent relentless majesty. Their legends credited Zeus with the power to reverse the course of the Sun from west to east, which he was supposed once to have done for some inscrutable reason affecting the succession at Mycenae, but they would have been astounded by our modern theory that it is the Earth which orbits the Sun. They saw exactly the same kind of phenomenon as we now see but they interpreted it differently.

Similarly the value of a ratio between two quantities may itself vary as a result of variation in either (or both) of these quantities. The variation in the ratio itself cannot give any indication as to the absolute variation in either of the quantities; nor, if only one quantity is varying can the ratio indicate which quantity this is.

We may now refer back to the paradox of comparative temperature measurements mentioned in Chapter 1. A ratio or other comparison of the mere magnitude of numbers representing measurements based upon an arbitrary scale cannot necessarily be interpreted as reflecting an equivalent comparison of the physical attributes measured.

Mathematics helps us to find out more and more about physical phenomena, but our seeming explanation of their occurrence is restricted to our own terms of reference. Our view of things changes as we ourselves change, or as we change our position or even, at the risk of being thought forward, close one eye. We must beware of thinking that it is the things we see which have necessarily changed. We cannot, Berkeley notwithstanding, destroy the solidity of the Earth and all its properties merely by closing both eyes.

Mathematics has indeed played an essential part in the development of other sciences as man gropes towards an understanding, attainable or not, of the universe; but it is paradoxical that, the greater is the power which mathematics gives us outside itself, so also the less do we seem to know about the structure of mathematics itself.

Before noting the more important of the theories on this topic it is desirable that the accidental discovery of independent mathematical properties be reconciled with the belief that mathematics is itself man-made. When the mathematician stumbles upon a new development, he cannot claim to have invented it; but neither is it logical to claim that, this being so, the development is necessarily the revelation of something which has and which always has had an existence outside the mathematical framework. The discovery is apparently the by-product of invention.

Invention and discovery can proceed in concert. The one does not exclude the other. They are indeed often indistinguishable, and it is perhaps less important to be able to distinguish one from the other than it is to understand clearly that discoveries are not of external or absolute truths but of properties inherent in inventions. Certainly as much ingenuity and inventiveness is needed for the discoveries as for the inventions.

If there were no triangles then their own peculiar properties could not exist. Who, when the idea of a triangle was first conceived, could have foreseen the ramifications of Pythagoras's Theorem or a whole theory of trigonometry based upon its properties?

It seems indisputable that triangles and other geometric figures are entirely the invention of man, since they are abstractions which exist only in the mind. We mentally join three straight lines and, presto! the rest follows like an explosion of invention. Nature left to herself would, so far as we can speculate, never produce a triangle whose sides are exactly straight. Nowhere in nature have we ever found, nor are we ever likely to find, a perfect circle.

Furthermore, while we may discuss the properties of triangles, we cannot represent them exactly in diagrams because their sides have no breadth. Even those representations which we do attempt suffer from the imperfections of our paper and drawing equipment. The circle is just as much an invention of the mind as is the principle of the compasses with which we seek, however unsuccessfully, to describe it.

And so, when he invented the triangle and the circle, man found that he had unwittingly invented their myriad properties. Mathematics was and is the conception of man, but it has taken a life unto itself just as the plot of a novel will sometimes take subtle control of the author's pen. The whole Euclidean geometry is derived by the axiomatic method from a very few basic axioms and postulates. It is truly astonishing just how much may be shown to be implicit in so little. Man created number but he never had control of it. Well might he stand amazed at what he has wrought.

The language of mathematics, like that of music, is universal. This itself may have suggested that there could be but one universal and absolute system of mathematical truths. Yet number evolved within the thoughts of man as also did the several languages which men now speak, although the manner in which these were first given birth will for ever be veiled from us.

The words and structure of language can not by any imaginative effort be thought to have been anything other than the invention of man. For, had this not been so, then every one of the world's inhabitants would speak the same absolute tongue; the languages themselves, the spellings and the meanings of words could not have altered as they have done throughout the centuries of time.

There is no one immutable tongue. There is no one immutable mathematics. This is a central view on which the modern belief rests, and it derives very largely from the developments noted first in non-Euclidean geometries. Just as there are many different spoken tongues within the overall concept of language, so also is it now realized that there are many different kinds of algebra and geometry and other structures within the overall concept of mathematics.

There are also alternative scales of notation for the expression of numbers. Some of the oddities of number behaviour stem from or are peculiar to the denary system in which we count in tens and powers of ten. This is the system in ordinary use in which a numeral of the form *abc* represents the quantity

$$100a + 10b + c$$

This is a convenient system, but it is no more the 'correct' notation than Latin is the 'correct' language.

The denary system is supposed to have been related to the number of our fingers. As he had ten fingers, man found it convenient to use these for counting, just as young children still do. It would stretch credulity to suggest that man was given ten fingers specifically so that he could count, as well as that he might eat and perhaps put them in other people's pies. Pythagoras indeed believed that the number 10, the holy Tetrakys, was divinely inspired. Perhaps man was also given ten toes so that he could check his fingering!

The Babylonians used a system based on the number 60, so they must presumably have gone into committee for the serious business of counting. In computers it is found more convenient to use the binary system in which numbers are expressed in powers of 2. We use the notation which is most convenient for our particular needs; no appeal can be made to external authority to validate any specific notation. The only criteria by which mathematics may be judged are its own bye-laws. This is a weakness to which we shall return a few pages hence.

Philosophers may well point out that, even if it be granted that mathematics is the product of man's thought, man himself has at best no more than a tenuous control over his thinking processes. Many of our ideas seem to stem from nowhere. This may to some extent reflect the highly sensitized receptivity of the mind which is conditioned by our surroundings and the subconscious interplay of thought. Most mathematical developments are preceded by a great deal of hard and frustrating mental effort; yet the vital link for which the mathematician seeks is more often than not revealed in a flash of insight when he is consciously thinking of some quite different subject.

Descartes is said to have received his idea of co-ordinate geometry in a dream. Poincaré has told how for fifteen days he strove to solve a particular problem; then one night, being unable to sleep as a result of drinking too much black coffee, 'ideas rose in crowds; I felt them collide until pairs interlocked, so to speak, making a stable combination'. By next morning much had been solved.

Poincaré believed that the subconscious or subliminal self plays an important role in mathematical creation, and that the sudden flash of illumination is a manifest sign of long subconscious working built upon the foundation of conscious effort. It seems that the subconscious works in much the same way as the conscious mind, but that it works more methodically, and therefore more successfully, because of its freedom from the subjective distractions of the conscious.

This effect is not peculiar only to mathematics. Most people will be familiar with the same kind of experience in everyday affairs. Problems which withstand all our conscious efforts are suddenly solved when we are apparently thinking of something else. At other times we find the desired solutions as soon as we return to the problems. This may in some measure be due to the more positive action of a refreshed and enlivened mind, but it also seems to result from the retention of the problem in the subconscious.

Whatever be the truth of this, the evidence still points to the remarkable potential of the human mind which often seems to work quite independently of our consciousness. Many of the mathematical prodigies who could perform miracles of mental calculations (such as Dase's multiplication of 79,532,853 by 93,758,479 in 54 seconds quoted in Ball's *Mathematical Recreations and Essays*) could not explain how they achieved their results.

All this, however, concerns the working of the mind and in no way helps to clarify just what mathematics really is. Granted that it is the product of man's mind, what is it that man has thus produced? Three main theories have been advanced in an attempt to throw light on this question although, as with all unprovable theories, there are also many intermediate or nonconformist opinions. In short, Logicism and Formalism regard mathematics as entirely independent of other disciplines and influences, whereas Intuitionism asserts that this is not so.

Logicism regards mathematics as a part of logic or as symbolized logic. But whereas mathematical method is based upon and employs logic, this does not necessarily mean that mathematics *is* logic, any more than a man who uses a knife and fork with his meal will, it is hoped, regard himself as either a knife or a fork. The logicist view was, perhaps, encouraged by the fact that logic may be symbolized and developed in much the same way as is possible with the symbols of mathematics. Insofar, however, as this symbolism of logic may truly be described as mathematical (and this is by no means certain) then it must seemingly be treated as an application of mathematics rather than as a welding together of logic and mathematics.

The symbolism of mathematics is also the bedrock of Formalism which asserts that mathematics is a formal logical system which is based only on logic and a consistent set of axioms. The symbols are regarded as being empty of all meaning other than their expression of or their conformity to the rules of mathematics. In this sense, mathematics is supposed to have some of the characteristics of an elaborate game with various specified 'moves' permissible.

Intuitionism on the other hand claims that at some stage in

mathematics there must be an appeal to experience or external influence, that it is in fact not possible to construct a completely self-contained mathematical system, and it rejects propositions which cannot be constructively demonstrated.

While it is probably true that the beginnings of mathematics were based upon external experience, and it is not possible to see how this could have been otherwise, nevertheless mathematics has come a long way since then and many useful departments have sprung up actually within mathematics itself. The fact that mathematics had its roots in experience does not necessarily imply that all its concepts must be traced back to those same roots.

It is arguable that the concept of number is itself suggested by some kind of external influence, but it cannot be maintained that all the multifarious properties which may be discovered in number relationships have anything to do with non-mathematical experience. Furthermore, while the concept of number may now seem to be part of our instinctive inheritance, this may only be because we have been brought up, from our earliest years, in a mathematical atmosphere created by number. Mathematics, like language, has to be learned. Yet, at the same time, it seems impossible to divorce mathematics and experience entirely. While some mathematical developments do not depend upon direct suggestion from experience, nevertheless other developments have indeed been directly suggested by experience.

The intuitionist rejects parts of mathematical 'truths' which the formalist accepts, and he holds much more stringent views on the question of what constitutes a valid mathematical proof. The intuitionist, for example, regards the unrestricted use of proof by *reductio ad absurdum* as little more than a cheap trick. Such a proof relies entirely upon the contention that if one proposition is correct, its opposite proposition is false, or that a proposition is itself either true or false, but not both.

The intuitionist points to the dangers of this method since not all problems are restricted to two possible and mutually exclusive and exhaustive solutions. In particular he claims that this form of classical logic was designed for use in finite mathematics, and that the paradoxes, which arise (as for example in Cantor's theories) in applying the same logical processes to infinite mathematics, arise in fact only because the arguments involved are not applicable to the infinite.

This view reflects closely that of Galileo's reflections already noted in Chapter 11. Whether one accepts Cantor's theories thus ultimately depends upon what philosophy of mathematics one accepts. Similarly the interpretation of proof, rigour and consistency will also depend upon whether we take an intuitionist or non-intuitionist view of mathematics.

Intuitionism would rid us of the paradoxes of the infinite but only at the expense of abandoning the structure in which the paradoxes occur and disinheriting a large part of mathematics. The severity of Intuitionism would exclude too much of what is otherwise pragmatically successful. One might just as well say that the only way to cure a sprained ankle is to amputate the leg – much too dear a price to pay.

The various schools of thought all agree on one point – mathematics is a consistent system. This, of course, applies to all scientific theories but theirs is only a provisional consistency which may be disproved by subsequent observations. Absolute consistency has always been regarded as having been built only into mathematics. This subject, however, provides a source of embarrassment to mathematics. How is it possible to be sure that mathematical propositions and theorems will never lead to contradictions merely because they have not yet done so? Is it not possible that we may eventually come across a contradiction? Attempts were made by the formalist school to prove that the formalism of mathematics is consistent and coherent, but they were eventually persuaded, by the publication of a remarkable demonstration by Gödel, that such attempts might just as well be abandoned.

Gödel's proof cannot be presented within a few lines, but its conclusion is that it is impossible to establish a proof of the consistency of a system unless the proof itself employs rules of inference which themselves will require to be proved consistent. The consistency of one system depends upon the consistency of another system and so, like the fleas of various sizes, *ad infinitum*. We are left with the hard proposition that even though, as we believe, a mathematical system may not lead to contradictions, nevertheless this cannot be demonstrated within the system itself.

This dilemma is of course apparent only to the mathematician who is concerned about the philosophical origins of his theories. The non-mathematician, who takes the whole of mathematics on trust will be completely unaware of it. The differing philosophies have had a profound effect upon mathematical thought but by and large they have not greatly affected the workings of mathematics. Twice two is still equal to four, and is never likely to be five.

It may seem strange that one may have a choice of philosophies of mathematics but, as is true of all philosophy, we have a choice only because no one philosophy can be shown to comprehend an absolute truth. Perhaps it is not even correct to call these philosophies as each deals only with certain aspects of mathematics. Not one of them takes us to the essence of mathematics, nor do they identify that common quality of things mathematical which distinguishes them from things non-mathematical. What, for instance, distinguishes music from mathematics? Though music has a mathematical content, nevertheless music is *not* mathematics.

Mathematics used to be regarded as the science of number and of magnitudes and measurements all of which could be expressed in number symbols. Number, then, was the qualifying mathematical characteristic. This is no longer true within the scope of what is now accepted as mathematics. Mathematics to-day – and perhaps this has always been true – may be described only as 'mathematics is what mathematicians do'. If a subject is so closely akin to mathematics that it is convenient to treat it as if it were part of mathematics, then there is no reason why this should be faulted. If we do not really know what mathematics is – if indeed it is an activity which can be described as a separate entity at all – then we can scarcely with any assurance exclude any such other subject from it.

On the other hand, the introduction of new subjects into the mathematical structure may well be an additional source of confusion. We have already observed that the use of logic in mathematics does not necessarily convert mathematics into logic or vice versa. It is also possible that set theory, which has been absorbed into mathematics with much alacrity, may cause the same kind of confusion. The logic of set theory has remarkable uses in mathematics, but this alone does not necessarily mean that set theory is essentially mathematical. It has an existence apart from its purely mathematical operations, as also have axiomatics and other logical forms.

These are specific examples of general scientific method which find significant expression in mathematics. This does not entitle mathematics to appropriate them as being peculiarly its own but they become so interwoven with the general structure that it is difficult to separate them from it. This is a problem in all aspects of life. Englishmen may live in France, but this does not of itself make them Frenchmen; as the years progress, however, their descendants will be as French as can be.

Many books have been written upon mathematical philosophy but, as Körner has commented, 'It may be that the question "what is mathematics?" does not admit of a single and simple answer and misleads us by suggesting such'. Neumann has noted 'a quite peculiar duplicity in the nature of mathematics', and expressed his disbelief that any simplified unified view of mathematics is possible without sacrificing its essence. And so, as it has also been observed, 'in spite of the certainty of its truths, it is by no means generally agreed of what, if anything, the true propositions of mathematics are true!'

Mathematicians have for centuries been building up the mathematical structure without any clear idea as to the nature of its foundations. This might be bad physical architecture, but it is apparently good mental mathematics. At any rate it has not yet tumbled all about us. The same may be said of all processes of thought until proved otherwise. Mathematics is no worse off, because of its insubstantial foundations, than are the other sciences. The dilemma is accentuated in mathematics only because this was supposed to be the one certain and exact science in an uncertain scientific world. Scientists who were obliged to admit that the assumptions and theories of their own researches were tenuously based upon inductive experience, had always been able to find a reflected security in their association with the seemingly inviolable concepts of mathematics. It was something of a shock to discover that the rules could be altered.

Yet the overall effect has not been to discredit the results of mathematics. The reliability of mathematical calculations employed in scientific applications were not automatically made suspect by any doubts which might be thrown upon the theoretical assumption either of mathematics or of its foundations. The effect rather was to add a degree of sharpness to scientific self-scrutiny and to liberate inventiveness in a more readily adventurous spirit of research.

The freeing of mathematics from the shackles of reality and the terrible responsibility as keeper of the absolute truth is thus seen to have had a profound effect upon mathematical thought. This influence also indirectly contributed to freedom of thought in other doctrines, spreading through the whole area of science and then into philosophy where its subtle effects helped to bring about changes in man's attitude to life itself. In art and music, for example, established form and tradition are no longer sacrosanct, although here there is evidence of a cheapening deterioration of standards from over-indulgence. Mathematics must beware of this reciprocal influence.

The effect of all this in religion is perhaps to confirm the convinced believer of the presumptions of science. Yet in fact it makes possible a removal of the conflict between faith and reason, though this is not to say that it reconciles them either. The puzzled thinker, who hitherto might have rejected religious tenets as unreasonable superstitions because reason seemed to offer a surer way to truth, now finds that this supposed alternative is non-existent. Reasoning alone cannot achieve this sublime aim.

The emancipation of the human intellect is of course nowhere more marked than it is within mathematics itself, for although the geometrical denouement constituted a sobering object lesson, it also threw into sharp focus the brilliant achievements of which the human mind is capable. What better evidence can there be of this than the immense and fantastically imaginative and aesthetically sophisticated concepts of mathematics now that it is realized that these spring directly from the extraordinary potential of the human intellect?

This mental origin itself probably precludes us from ever really understanding the full and precise nature of mathematics since the mind should perhaps not be expected to be able to understand its own inner working. Perhaps, too, this is just as well. If man could justifiably claim that he had invented the whole of mathematics, that there was nothing in mathematics which he had not built into it, and that he understood it all perfectly, we could still have wondered at the achievement but the mystery of mathematics would have disappeared.

Epilogue

In the cosmic scale of time, Einstein notwithstanding, the tomb-stone is only slightly more durable than the human frame it covers, yet there have been a number of instances of mathe-maticians wishing to commemorate, if not to perpetuate, their fondest discoveries in the writing of the stonemason's chisel.

Archimedes was intrigued by the discovery that the ratio 2:3 between the volume of a sphere and the volume of its circum-scribed cylinder is the same as the ratio of string-lengths involved in the perfect fifth musical interval.

The significance of this particular relationship may escape our supposedly greater sophistication, although in itself the ratio between the volumes of the sphere and its circumscribed cylinder is remarkable enough even if it has a simple mathematical explanation. Since each of the quantities representing these respective volumes involves the quantity π, neither of them can be calculated exactly, yet the ratio between them may be stated precisely and simply by the two smallest whole numbers other than unity.

Possibly it was this emergence of the apparent significance of whole numbers where their influence was not intuitively to be expected which forged for Archimedes the vital link between geometry, arithmetic and music.

Archimedes asked that the design of a sphere and circum-scribed cylinder be inscribed upon his tombstone. Cicero seems to have found the stone so inscribed in about 75 B.C. but then to have carelessly lost it again. The tomb currently pointed out to eager tourists, as they rush through Syracuse, as being the tomb of Archimedes unfortunately does not possess this requisite identifying hallmark.

Gauss, too, expressed a similar last wish. Of all his many dis-coveries, the one which delighted him most was the discovery of the relationship between Fermat Numbers and the properties of certain polygons. Using only a straightedge and compass, it is possible to inscribe a regular polygon, with an odd number (*n*) of sides, within a circle only if *n* is a prime Fermat Number or is a product of two or more different such prime numbers.

The only known prime Fermat Numbers are 3, 5, 17, 257 and 65537. Gauss established his proposition entirely by algebra. Within his own lifetime a satisfactory geometrical method for the construction of an inscribed heptadecagon (polygon with seven-teen sides) had been devised. The particular discovery that the heptadecagon could be constructed and that the geometrical fact had first been demonstrated by algebra so delighted Gauss that, according to Sartorius, it decided him to dedicate his life to mathematics. He asked that an inscribed heptadecagon should be designed on his tombstone, but his wishes were for some reason not carried out. Perhaps none of his friends could chip out the stone and none of the available masons could master the geo-metry required. Nevertheless, the design was subsequently in-cluded in a monument erected to his memory in Braunschweig, the place of his birth.

Ludolf van Ceulen, who calculated the value of π to 35 decimal places, requested that this should be engraved on his tomb, and this was apparently done. It is perhaps just as well that William Shanks, who calculated the value of π to 707 decimal places, did not make a similar request, and that Gauss did not ask for the polygon of 65537 sides!

Jacob Bernoulli, who discovered many of the properties of the logarithmic or equiangular spiral, was fascinated by its peculiar symmetry wherein curves derived from it reproduce the original curve. Bernoulli, who was also something of a mystic, combined his mathematical and mystical interests in the instruction that the spiral should be inscribed on his memorial accompanied by the words *Eadem mutata resurgo* – 'though changed, I shall arise the same'.

To each of these men the designs of their delight must in their lifetime have taken on a significance such as was implicit in the earlier heraldic devices or even perhaps, more mystically, a supposed philosophical significance similar to, but of a more personal character than that of the Pythagorean Pentagram.

Each design incorporated some mathematical revelation, and the desire to have their tombstones decorated in this way is a sure indication of what these revelations must have meant to their discoverers. This desire may also, perhaps, be seen as a sign of the human weakness of pride, but these men were entitled to be proud of their achievements and would in any case not have wished to appear less human than the rest of us. We have previously noted in Chapter 8 that the more impetuous and possibly less morbidly minded Hamilton did not wait for the last rites to be performed before carving an appropriate commemorative formula in the stonework of a bridge. This he carved in the white heat of discovery.

The true monuments, however, to the genius of mathematical giants are to be found not in their cold memorial stones, whether decorated or not, nor in the defacements of public highways but in the mathematical heritage which they bequeathed to succeeding generations. Their genius is stilled, but their spirit is eternal. The mystery of mathematics outlasted them and will outlast each and every one of us.

Index

Penguinews and Penguins in Print

Our illustrated magazine *Penguinews* appears every month; it contains details of all the latest Penguins, Pelicans and Puffins.

Penguinews always contains an article on a major author, plus many other items of interest.

To supplement *Penguinews* we have *Penguins in Print*, a complete list of all available Penguins titles . . . there are now over four thousand to choose from.

We can send you a free copy of the current *Penguinews*, if you like.

And if you want to receive both publications regularly just send us 30p (if you live in the United Kingdom) or 60p (if you live elsewhere), for a year's issues. A cheque or a postal order will do.

Write to Dept EP, Penguin Books Ltd, Harmondsworth, Middlesex, and we'll add your name to our mailing list.

Note: *Penguinews* and *Penguins in Print* are not available in the U.S.A. or Canada

Mathematical Puzzles and Diversions

Edited by Martin Gardner

Whether you are intrigued, embarrassed, or just plain
scared by the complexities of mathematics, this is a book
which will both delight and infuriate you. Culled from the
pages of *Scientific American*, these puzzles, problems,
and paradoxes, with names like Hexaflexagons,
Polyominoes, and the Icosian Game, are the work of a
master and the best of their kind. But a word of warning.
This beguiling collection has been specially designed to
seduce you for hours, days, weeks, from the duller
business of practical life. Be on your guard!

'This book is a "must" for the school and college library
and will worthily find a place on the shelves of
mathematical teachers' – *Technical Education*

Also by Martin Gardner
More Mathematical Puzzles and Diversions

And two Penguins
The Annotated Alice
The Annotated Snark

Not for sale in the U.S.A. or Canada

Introducing Mathematics 1
VISION IN ELEMENTARY MATHEMATICS

W. W. Sawyer

Anyone who has read *Mathematician's Delight* or *Prelude to Mathematics* knows W. W. Sawyer as a mathematical lion-tamer. Figures do not merely come to life for him: they eat out of his hand.

Here he once again presents elementary mathematics in the most graphic and least terrifying way possible. As he early observes, we most of us possess a direct vision which allows us to 'see' the smaller numbers. But how to organize in our minds the chaos that lies beyond the smallest numbers is a problem that confronts the entire human race. In tackling this problem, both for those who find figures fun and, especially, for those who may be called on to teach, W. W. Sawyer offers to a wider circle methods which are already used by many good teachers – methods of visualizing, dramatizing, and analysing numbers so that the attention and understanding of children can be gained and held.

There is a boom in mathematics today. Anyone, from parent to part-time teacher, may at any moment need to understand problems in elementary arithmetic or algebra. This lively and human book can help enormously to lighten the task.

Also available

Mathematician's Delight

W. W. Sawyer

This volume is designed to convince the general reader that mathematics is not a forbidding science but an attractive mental exercise. Its success in this intention is confirmed by some of the reviews it received on its first appearance:

'It may be recommended with confidence for the light it throws upon the discovery and application of many common mathematical operations' – *The Times Literary Supplement*

'It jumps to life from the start, and sets the reader off with his mind working intelligently and with interest. It relates mathematics to life and thought and points out the value of the practical approach by reminding us that the Pyramids were built on Euclid's principles three thousand years before Euclid thought of them' – *John O'London's*

'The writer clearly not only loves his subject but has unusual gifts as a teacher ... from start to finish the reader, whose own interests and training may lie in very different fields, can follow the thread' – *Financial News*

Also by W. W. Sawyer
Prelude to Mathematics

Also by W. J. Reichmann

Use and Abuse of Statistics

Without statistics much of the machinery of modern life would grind slowly to a standstill. The subject which is said to have prompted Disraeli to quip: 'There are three sorts of lie: lies, damned lies, and statistics', is nevertheless an essential tool in science, industry, commerce, and other fields.

In this book a Fellow of the Royal Statistical Society introduces the reader in readily comprehensible terms to the world of averages, probabilities, percentages, indexes, samples, and trends. Explaining the meaning of such expressions, the author shows how and for what purposes statistics may usefully be employed and how they should certainly not be employed. The results is not a textbook but an introductory discussion of a fascinating application of mathematics, to stimulate the student or explain to the general reader just what statistics is all about.

'The really important part of the book – and at this level it is the best I have read on the subject – is his discussion of what statistics is, and does . . . this book will prove a boon' – *Financial Times*